THIS BOOK BELONG

CONTACT INFORMATION

NAME:	
ADDRESS:	
PHONE:	

Copyright © 2021

SCORE BOOK

BASEBALL

TEAM LINE UP

TEAM	OPPOSING TEAM
COACH	COACH

	NO.	STARTERS	POS.
1			
2			
3			
4			
5			
6			
7			
8			
9			
10			
11			
12			
13			
14			
15			
16			
17			

NO.	SUBSTITUTES	POS

NOTES

DATE	TIME	FIELD

TEAM LINE UP

TEAM		OPPOSING TEAM	
COACH		COACH	

	NO.	STARTERS	POS.
1			
2			
3			
4			
5			
6			
7			
8			
9			
10			
11			
12			
13			
14			
15			
16			
17			

NO.	SUBSTITUTES	POS

NOTES

DATE	TIME	FIELD

BASEBALL / SOFTBALL SCORESHEET

	#	PLAYER	POS	1	2	3	4	5	6	7	8	9
1												
SUB.												
2												
SUB.												
3												
SUB.												
4												
SUB.												
5												
SUB.												
6												
SUB.												
7												
SUB.												
8												
SUB.												
9												
SUB.												
10												
SUB.												
11												
SUB.												
12												
SUB.												
13												
SUB.												
14												
SUB.												
15												
SUB.												
16												
SUB.												
17												
SUB.												TOTALS

Each batting cell contains: 1B 2B 3B HR BB with a diamond diagram.

INNING TOTALS	RUNS									
	HITS									
	ERRORS									
	LEFT ON BASE									

AB	R	H	RBI	BB	SO	PLAYER #			
						1 / 1 / 1 / 1			
						2 / 2 / 2 / 2			
						3 / 3 / 3 / 3			
						... (1–100)			

	PITCHER	W	L	S	IP	BF	H	R	ER	BB	SO
	TOTALS										

PITCHES BY INNING	1	2	3	4	5	6	7	8	9
TOTALS									

NOTES

NOTES

PITCH COUNT TOTALS

FINAL SCORE		
HOME		VISITOR
	RUNS	
	HITS	
	ERRORS	
UMPIRES		
SCORER		

TEAM LINE UP

TEAM		OPPOSING TEAM	
COACH		COACH	

	NO.	STARTERS	POS.
1			
2			
3			
4			
5			
6			
7			
8			
9			
10			
11			
12			
13			
14			
15			
16			
17			

NO.	SUBSTITUTES	POS

NOTES		
DATE	TIME	FIELD

TEAM LINE UP

TEAM	OPPOSING TEAM
COACH	COACH

	NO.	STARTERS	POS.
1			
2			
3			
4			
5			
6			
7			
8			
9			
10			
11			
12			
13			
14			
15			
16			
17			

NO.	SUBSTITUTES	POS

NOTES		
DATE	TIME	FIELD

BASEBALL / SOFTBALL SCORESHEET

	#	PLAYER	POS	1	2	3	4	5	6	7	8	9	
1													
SUB.													
2													
SUB.													
3													
SUB.													
4													
SUB.													
5													
SUB.													
6													
SUB.													
7													
SUB.													
8													
SUB.													
9													
SUB.													
10													
SUB.													
11													
SUB.													
12													
SUB.													
13													
SUB.													
14													
SUB.													
15													
SUB.													
16													
SUB.													
17													TOTALS
SUB.													

Each batter box header: 1B 2B 3B HR BB

INNING TOTALS	RUNS									
	HITS									
	ERRORS									
	LEFT ON BASE									

AB	R	H	RBI	BB	SO	PLAYER #			
						1	1	1	1
						2	2	2	2
						3	3	3	3
						4	4	4	4
						5	5	5	5
						6	6	6	6
						7	7	7	7
						8	8	8	8
						9	9	9	9
						10	10	10	10
						11	11	11	11
						12	12	12	12
						13	13	13	13
						14	14	14	14
						15	15	15	15
						16	16	16	16
						17	17	17	17
						18	18	18	18
						19	19	19	19
						20	20	20	20
						21	21	21	21
						22	22	22	22
						23	23	23	23
						24	24	24	24
						25	25	25	25
						26	26	26	26
						27	27	27	27
						28	28	28	28
						29	29	29	29
						30	30	30	30
						31	31	31	31
						32	32	32	32
						33	33	33	33
						34	34	34	34
						35	35	35	35
						36	36	36	36
						37	37	37	37
						38	38	38	38
						39	39	39	39
						40	40	40	40
						41	41	41	41
						42	42	42	42
						43	43	43	43
						44	44	44	44
						45	45	45	45
						46	46	46	46
						47	47	47	47
						48	48	48	48
						49	49	49	49
						50	50	50	50
						51	51	51	51
						52	52	52	52
						53	53	53	53
						54	54	54	54
						55	55	55	55
						56	56	56	56
						57	57	57	57
						58	58	58	58
						59	59	59	59
						60	60	60	60
						61	61	61	61
						62	62	62	62
						63	63	63	63
						64	64	64	64
						65	65	65	65
						66	66	66	66
						67	67	67	67
						68	68	68	68
						69	69	69	69
						70	70	70	70
						71	71	71	71
						72	72	72	72
						73	73	73	73
						74	74	74	74
						75	75	75	75
						76	76	76	76
						77	77	77	77
						78	78	78	78
						79	79	79	79
						80	80	80	80
						81	81	81	81
						82	82	82	82
						83	83	83	83
						84	84	84	84
						85	85	85	85
						86	86	86	86
						87	87	87	87
						88	88	88	88
						89	89	89	89
						90	90	90	90
						91	91	91	91
						92	92	92	92
						93	93	93	93
						94	94	94	94
						95	95	95	95
						96	96	96	96
						97	97	97	97
						98	98	98	98
						99	99	99	99
						100	100	100	100

NOTES

PITCH COUNT TOTALS

#	PITCHER	W	L	S	IP	BF	H	R	ER	BB	SO
	TOTALS										

PITCHES BY INNING	1	2	3	4	5	6	7	8	9
TOTALS									

NOTES

FINAL SCORE

HOME		VISITOR
	RUNS	
	HITS	
	ERRORS	
UMPIRES		
SCORER		

TEAM LINE UP

TEAM		OPPOSING TEAM	
COACH		COACH	

	NO.	STARTERS	POS.		NO.	SUBSTITUTES	POS
1							
2							
3							
4							
5							
6							
7							
8							
9							
10							
11							
12							
13							
14							
15							
16							
17							

NOTES		
DATE	TIME	FIELD

TEAM LINE UP

TEAM	OPPOSING TEAM
COACH	COACH

	NO.	STARTERS	POS.
1			
2			
3			
4			
5			
6			
7			
8			
9			
10			
11			
12			
13			
14			
15			
16			
17			

NO.	SUBSTITUTES	POS

NOTES		
DATE	TIME	FIELD

BASEBALL / SOFTBALL SCORESHEET

	#	PLAYER	POS	1	2	3	4	5	6	7	8	9
1												
SUB.												
2												
SUB.												
3												
SUB.												
4												
SUB.												
5												
SUB.												
6												
SUB.												
7												
SUB.												
8												
SUB.												
9												
SUB.												
10												
SUB.												
11												
SUB.												
12												
SUB.												
13												
SUB.												
14												
SUB.												
15												
SUB.												
16												
SUB.												
17												
SUB.												TOTALS

INNING TOTALS	RUNS									
	HITS									
	ERRORS									
	LEFT ON BASE									

AB	R	H	RBI	BB	SO	PLAYER #			
						1	1	1	1
						2	2	2	2
						3	3	3	3
						4	4	4	4
						5	5	5	5
						6	6	6	6
						7	7	7	7
						8	8	8	8
						9	9	9	9
						10	10	10	10
						11	11	11	11
						12	12	12	12
						13	13	13	13
						14	14	14	14
						15	15	15	15
						16	16	16	16
						17	17	17	17
						18	18	18	18
						19	19	19	19
						20	20	20	20
						21	21	21	21
						22	22	22	22
						23	23	23	23
						24	24	24	24
						25	25	25	25
						26	26	26	26
						27	27	27	27
						28	28	28	28
						29	29	29	29
						30	30	30	30
						31	31	31	31
						32	32	32	32
						33	33	33	33
						34	34	34	34
						35	35	35	35
						36	36	36	36
						37	37	37	37
						38	38	38	38
						39	39	39	39
						40	40	40	40
						41	41	41	41
						42	42	42	42
						43	43	43	43
						44	44	44	44
						45	45	45	45
						46	46	46	46
						47	47	47	47
						48	48	48	48
						49	49	49	49
						50	50	50	50
						51	51	51	51
						52	52	52	52
						53	53	53	53
						54	54	54	54
						55	55	55	55
						56	56	56	56
						57	57	57	57
						58	58	58	58
						59	59	59	59
						60	60	60	60
						61	61	61	61
						62	62	62	62
						63	63	63	63
						64	64	64	64
						65	65	65	65
						66	66	66	66
						67	67	67	67
						68	68	68	68
						69	69	69	69
						70	70	70	70
						71	71	71	71
						72	72	72	72
						73	73	73	73
						74	74	74	74
						75	75	75	75
						76	76	76	76
						77	77	77	77
						78	78	78	78
						79	79	79	79
						80	80	80	80
						81	81	81	81
						82	82	82	82
						83	83	83	83
						84	84	84	84
						85	85	85	85
						86	86	86	86
						87	87	87	87
						88	88	88	88
						89	89	89	89
						90	90	90	90
						91	91	91	91
						92	92	92	92
						93	93	93	93
						94	94	94	94
						95	95	95	95
						96	96	96	96
						97	97	97	97
						98	98	98	98
						99	99	99	99
						100	100	100	100

NOTES

PITCH COUNT TOTALS

#	PITCHER	W	L	S	IP	BF	H	R	ER	BB	SO
	TOTALS										

PITCHES BY INNING	1	2	3	4	5	6	7	8	9
TOTALS									

NOTES

FINAL SCORE		
HOME		VISITOR
	RUNS	
	HITS	
	ERRORS	
UMPIRES		
SCORER		

TEAM LINE UP

TEAM	OPPOSING TEAM
COACH	COACH

	NO.	STARTERS	POS.
1			
2			
3			
4			
5			
6			
7			
8			
9			
10			
11			
12			
13			
14			
15			
16			
17			

NO.	SUBSTITUTES	POS

NOTES

DATE	TIME	FIELD

TEAM LINE UP

TEAM	OPPOSING TEAM
COACH	COACH

	NO.	STARTERS	POS.
1			
2			
3			
4			
5			
6			
7			
8			
9			
10			
11			
12			
13			
14			
15			
16			
17			

NO.	SUBSTITUTES	POS

NOTES

DATE	TIME	FIELD

BASEBALL / SOFTBALL SCORESHEET

	#	PLAYER	POS	1	2	3	4	5	6	7	8	9
1												
SUB.												
2												
SUB.												
3												
SUB.												
4												
SUB.												
5												
SUB.												
6												
SUB.												
7												
SUB.												
8												
SUB.												
9												
SUB.												
10												
SUB.												
11												
SUB.												
12												
SUB.												
13												
SUB.												
14												
SUB.												
15												
SUB.												
16												
SUB.												
17												
SUB.												TOTALS

Each diamond cell marked: 1B 2B 3B HR BB

INNING TOTALS	RUNS									
	HITS									
	ERRORS									
	LEFT ON BASE									

AB	R	H	RBI	BB	SO		PLAYER #			

Left table header columns: AB, R, H, RBI, BB, SO, and PLAYER # section with columns showing numbers 1–100.

The PLAYER # columns each list numbers 1 through 100:

1, 2, 3, 4, 5, 6, 7, 8, 9, 10, 11, 12, 13, 14, 15, 16, 17, 18, 19, 20, 21, 22, 23, 24, 25, 26, 27, 28, 29, 30, 31, 32, 33, 34, 35, 36, 37, 38, 39, 40, 41, 42, 43, 44, 45, 46, 47, 48, 49, 50, 51, 52, 53, 54, 55, 56, 57, 58, 59, 60, 61, 62, 63, 64, 65, 66, 67, 68, 69, 70, 71, 72, 73, 74, 75, 76, 77, 78, 79, 80, 81, 82, 83, 84, 85, 86, 87, 88, 89, 90, 91, 92, 93, 94, 95, 96, 97, 98, 99, 100

NOTES

PITCH COUNT TOTALS

!"#$ %#"&#"#()$ $*!'#()$

+($.!

~)$'

/(%(#·&'

#	PITCHER	W	L	S	IP	BF	H	R	ER	BB	SO
	TOTALS										

PITCHES BY INNING	1	2	3	4	5	6	7	8	9
TOTALS									

NOTES

FINAL SCORE

HOME		VISITOR
	RUNS	
	HITS	
	ERRORS	
UMPIRES		
SCORER		

TEAM LINE UP

TEAM	OPPOSING TEAM
COACH	COACH

	NO.	STARTERS	POS.
1			
2			
3			
4			
5			
6			
7			
8			
9			
10			
11			
12			
13			
14			
15			
16			
17			

NO.	SUBSTITUTES	POS

NOTES

DATE	TIME	FIELD

TEAM LINE UP

TEAM	OPPOSING TEAM
COACH	COACH

	NO.	STARTERS	POS.		NO.	SUBSTITUTES	POS
1							
2							
3							
4							
5							
6							
7							
8							
9							
10							
11							
12							
13							
14							
15							
16							
17							

NOTES		
DATE	TIME	FIELD

BASEBALL / SOFTBALL SCORESHEET

	#	PLAYER	POS	1	2	3	4	5	6	7	8	9
1												
SUB.												
2												
SUB.												
3												
SUB.												
4												
SUB.												
5												
SUB.												
6												
SUB.												
7												
SUB.												
8												
SUB.												
9												
SUB.												
10												
SUB.												
11												
SUB.												
12												
SUB.												
13												
SUB.												
14												
SUB.												
15												
SUB.												
16												
SUB.												
17												
SUB.												TOTALS

INNING TOTALS	RUNS									
	HITS									
	ERRORS									
	LEFT ON BASE									

AB	R	H	RBI	BB	SO		PLAYER #			
							1	1	1	1
							2	2	2	2
							3	3	3	3
							4	4	4	4
							5	5	5	5
							6	6	6	6
							7	7	7	7
							8	8	8	8
							9	9	9	9
							10	10	10	10
							11	11	11	11
							12	12	12	12
							13	13	13	13
							14	14	14	14
							15	15	15	15
							16	16	16	16
							17	17	17	17
							18	18	18	18
							19	19	19	19
							20	20	20	20
							21	21	21	21
							22	22	22	22
							23	23	23	23
							24	24	24	24
							25	25	25	25
							26	26	26	26
							27	27	27	27
							28	28	28	28
							29	29	29	29
							30	30	30	30
							31	31	31	31
							32	32	32	32
							33	33	33	33
							34	34	34	34
							35	35	35	35
							36	36	36	36
							37	37	37	37
							38	38	38	38
							39	39	39	39
							40	40	40	40
							41	41	41	41
							42	42	42	42
							43	43	43	43
							44	44	44	44
							45	45	45	45
							46	46	46	46
							47	47	47	47
							48	48	48	48
							49	49	49	49
							50	50	50	50
							51	51	51	51
							52	52	52	52
							53	53	53	53
							54	54	54	54
							55	55	55	55
							56	56	56	56
							57	57	57	57
							58	58	58	58
							59	59	59	59
							60	60	60	60
							61	61	61	61
							62	62	62	62
							63	63	63	63
							64	64	64	64
							65	65	65	65
							66	66	66	66
							67	67	67	67
							68	68	68	68
							69	69	69	69
							70	70	70	70
							71	71	71	71
							72	72	72	72
							73	73	73	73
							74	74	74	74
							75	75	75	75
							76	76	76	76
							77	77	77	77
							78	78	78	78
							79	79	79	79
							80	80	80	80
							81	81	81	81
							82	82	82	82
							83	83	83	83
							84	84	84	84
							85	85	85	85
							86	86	86	86
							87	87	87	87
							88	88	88	88
							89	89	89	89
							90	90	90	90
							91	91	91	91
							92	92	92	92
							93	93	93	93
							94	94	94	94
							95	95	95	95
							96	96	96	96
							97	97	97	97
							98	98	98	98
							99	99	99	99
							100	100	100	100

NOTES

PITCH COUNT TOTALS

#	PITCHER	W	L	S	IP	BF	H	R	ER	BB	SO
	TOTALS										

PITCHES BY INNING	1	2	3	4	5	6	7	8	9
TOTALS									

NOTES

FINAL SCORE

HOME		VISITOR
	RUNS	
	HITS	
	ERRORS	
UMPIRES		
SCORER		

TEAM LINE UP

TEAM	OPPOSING TEAM
COACH	COACH

	NO.	STARTERS	POS.
1			
2			
3			
4			
5			
6			
7			
8			
9			
10			
11			
12			
13			
14			
15			
16			
17			

NO.	SUBSTITUTES	POS

NOTES		
DATE	TIME	FIELD

TEAM LINE UP

TEAM		OPPOSING TEAM	
COACH		COACH	

	NO.	STARTERS	POS.
1			
2			
3			
4			
5			
6			
7			
8			
9			
10			
11			
12			
13			
14			
15			
16			
17			

NO.	SUBSTITUTES	POS

NOTES		
DATE	TIME	FIELD

BASEBALL / SOFTBALL SCORESHEET

	#	PLAYER	POS	1	2	3	4	5	6	7	8	9
1												
SUB.												
2												
SUB.												
3												
SUB.												
4												
SUB.												
5												
SUB.												
6												
SUB.												
7												
SUB.												
8												
SUB.												
9												
SUB.												
10												
SUB.												
11												
SUB.												
12												
SUB.												
13												
SUB.												
14												
SUB.												
15												
SUB.												
16												
SUB.												
17												
SUB.												TOTALS

Batting cells labeled: 1B 2B 3B HR BB

INNING TOTALS	RUNS									
	HITS									
	ERRORS									
	LEFT ON BASE									

AB	R	H	RBI	BB	SO		PLAYER #			
							1	1	1	1
							2	2	2	2
							3	3	3	3
							4	4	4	4
							5	5	5	5
							6	6	6	6
							7	7	7	7
							8	8	8	8
							9	9	9	9
							10	10	10	10
							11	11	11	11
							12	12	12	12
							13	13	13	13
							14	14	14	14
							15	15	15	15
							16	16	16	16
							17	17	17	17
							18	18	18	18
							19	19	19	19
							20	20	20	20
							21	21	21	21
							22	22	22	22
							23	23	23	23
							24	24	24	24
							25	25	25	25
							26	26	26	26
							27	27	27	27
							28	28	28	28
							29	29	29	29
							30	30	30	30
							31	31	31	31
							32	32	32	32
							33	33	33	33
							34	34	34	34
							35	35	35	35
							36	36	36	36
							37	37	37	37
							38	38	38	38
							39	39	39	39
							40	40	40	40
							41	41	41	41
							42	42	42	42
							43	43	43	43
							44	44	44	44
							45	45	45	45
							46	46	46	46
							47	47	47	47
							48	48	48	48
							49	49	49	49
							50	50	50	50
							51	51	51	51
							52	52	52	52
							53	53	53	53
							54	54	54	54
							55	55	55	55
							56	56	56	56
							57	57	57	57
							58	58	58	58
							59	59	59	59
							60	60	60	60
							61	61	61	61
							62	62	62	62
							63	63	63	63
							64	64	64	64
							65	65	65	65
							66	66	66	66
							67	67	67	67
							68	68	68	68
							69	69	69	69
							70	70	70	70
							71	71	71	71
							72	72	72	72
							73	73	73	73
							74	74	74	74
							75	75	75	75
							76	76	76	76
							77	77	77	77
							78	78	78	78
							79	79	79	79
							80	80	80	80
							81	81	81	81
							82	82	82	82
							83	83	83	83
							84	84	84	84
							85	85	85	85
							86	86	86	86
							87	87	87	87
							88	88	88	88
							89	89	89	89
							90	90	90	90
							91	91	91	91
							92	92	92	92
							93	93	93	93
							94	94	94	94
							95	95	95	95
							96	96	96	96
							97	97	97	97
							98	98	98	98
							99	99	99	99
							100	100	100	100

NOTES

PITCH COUNT TOTALS

!"#$	%6#"&#"#()$		$*!#()$
+($.!			
-)$'			
/(%6(#.&'			

#	PITCHER	W	L	S	IP	BF	H	R	ER	BB	SO
	TOTALS										

PITCHES BY INNING	1	2	3	4	5	6	7	8	9
TOTALS									

NOTES

FINAL SCORE	
HOME	VISITOR
	RUNS	
	HITS	
	ERRORS	
UMPIRES	
SCORER	

TEAM LINE UP

TEAM	OPPOSING TEAM
COACH	COACH

	NO.	STARTERS	POS.		NO.	SUBSTITUTES	POS
1							
2							
3							
4							
5							
6							
7							
8							
9							
10							
11							
12							
13							
14							
15							
16							
17							

NOTES

DATE	TIME	FIELD

TEAM LINE UP

TEAM	OPPOSING TEAM
COACH	COACH

	NO.	STARTERS	POS.		NO.	SUBSTITUTES	POS
1							
2							
3							
4							
5							
6							
7							
8							
9							
10							
11							
12							
13							
14							
15							
16							
17							

NOTES

DATE	TIME	FIELD

BASEBALL / SOFTBALL SCORESHEET

	#	PLAYER	POS	1	2	3	4	5	6	7	8	9
1												
SUB.												
2												
SUB.												
3												
SUB.												
4												
SUB.												
5												
SUB.												
6												
SUB.												
7												
SUB.												
8												
SUB.												
9												
SUB.												
10												
SUB.												
11												
SUB.												
12												
SUB.												
13												
SUB.												
14												
SUB.												
15												
SUB.												
16												
SUB.												
17												
SUB.												TOTALS

Each cell contains: 1B 2B 3B HR BB with baseball diamond diagram

INNING TOTALS	RUNS										
	HITS										
	ERRORS										
	LEFT ON BASE										

AB	R	H	RBI	BB	SO	PLAYER #			
						1	1	1	1
						2	2	2	2
						3	3	3	3
						4	4	4	4
						5	5	5	5
						6	6	6	6
						7	7	7	7
						8	8	8	8
						9	9	9	9
						10	10	10	10
						11	11	11	11
						12	12	12	12
						13	13	13	13
						14	14	14	14
						15	15	15	15
						16	16	16	16
						17	17	17	17
						18	18	18	18
						19	19	19	19
						20	20	20	20
						21	21	21	21
						22	22	22	22
						23	23	23	23
						24	24	24	24
						25	25	25	25
						26	26	26	26
						27	27	27	27
						28	28	28	28
						29	29	29	29
						30	30	30	30
						31	31	31	31
						32	32	32	32
						33	33	33	33
						34	34	34	34
						35	35	35	35
						36	36	36	36
						37	37	37	37
						38	38	38	38
						39	39	39	39
						40	40	40	40
						41	41	41	41
						42	42	42	42
						43	43	43	43
						44	44	44	44
						45	45	45	45
						46	46	46	46
						47	47	47	47
						48	48	48	48
						49	49	49	49
						50	50	50	50
						51	51	51	51
						52	52	52	52
						53	53	53	53
						54	54	54	54
						55	55	55	55
						56	56	56	56
						57	57	57	57
						58	58	58	58
						59	59	59	59
						60	60	60	60
						61	61	61	61
						62	62	62	62
						63	63	63	63
						64	64	64	64
						65	65	65	65
						66	66	66	66
						67	67	67	67
						68	68	68	68
						69	69	69	69
						70	70	70	70
						71	71	71	71
						72	72	72	72
						73	73	73	73
						74	74	74	74
						75	75	75	75
						76	76	76	76
						77	77	77	77
						78	78	78	78
						79	79	79	79
						80	80	80	80
						81	81	81	81
						82	82	82	82
						83	83	83	83
						84	84	84	84
						85	85	85	85
						86	86	86	86
						87	87	87	87
						88	88	88	88
						89	89	89	89
						90	90	90	90
						91	91	91	91
						92	92	92	92
						93	93	93	93
						94	94	94	94
						95	95	95	95
						96	96	96	96
						97	97	97	97
						98	98	98	98
						99	99	99	99
						100	100	100	100

NOTES

PITCH COUNT TOTALS

#	PITCHER	W	L	S	IP	BF	H	R	ER	BB	SO
	TOTALS										

PITCHES BY INNING	1	2	3	4	5	6	7	8	9
TOTALS									

NOTES

FINAL SCORE	
HOME	VISITOR
	RUNS	
	HITS	
	ERRORS	
UMPIRES	
SCORER	

TEAM LINE UP

TEAM		OPPOSING TEAM	
COACH		COACH	

	NO.	STARTERS	POS.
1			
2			
3			
4			
5			
6			
7			
8			
9			
10			
11			
12			
13			
14			
15			
16			
17			

NO.	SUBSTITUTES	POS

NOTES

DATE	TIME	FIELD

TEAM LINE UP

TEAM		OPPOSING TEAM	
COACH		COACH	

	NO.	STARTERS	POS.		NO.	SUBSTITUTES	POS
1							
2							
3							
4							
5							
6							
7							
8							
9							
10							
11							
12							
13							
14							
15							
16							
17							

NOTES		
DATE	TIME	FIELD

BASEBALL / SOFTBALL SCORESHEET

	#	PLAYER	POS	1	2	3	4	5	6	7	8	9
1												
SUB.												
2												
SUB.												
3												
SUB.												
4												
SUB.												
5												
SUB.												
6												
SUB.												
7												
SUB.												
8												
SUB.												
9												
SUB.												
10												
SUB.												
11												
SUB.												
12												
SUB.												
13												
SUB.												
14												
SUB.												
15												
SUB.												
16												
SUB.												
17												
SUB.												TOTALS

INNING TOTALS	RUNS									
	HITS									
	ERRORS									
	LEFT ON BASE									

Each batter cell contains: 1B 2B 3B HR BB

AB	R	H	RBI	BB	SO		PLAYER #			
							1	1	1	1
							2	2	2	2
							3	3	3	3
							4	4	4	4
							5	5	5	5
							6	6	6	6
							7	7	7	7
							8	8	8	8
							9	9	9	9
							10	10	10	10
							11	11	11	11
							12	12	12	12
							13	13	13	13
							14	14	14	14
							15	15	15	15
							16	16	16	16
							17	17	17	17
							18	18	18	18
							19	19	19	19
							20	20	20	20
							21	21	21	21
							22	22	22	22
							23	23	23	23
							24	24	24	24
							25	25	25	25
							26	26	26	26
							27	27	27	27
							28	28	28	28
							29	29	29	29
							30	30	30	30
							31	31	31	31
							32	32	32	32
							33	33	33	33
							34	34	34	34
							35	35	35	35
							36	36	36	36
							37	37	37	37
							38	38	38	38
							39	39	39	39
							40	40	40	40
							41	41	41	41
							42	42	42	42
							43	43	43	43
							44	44	44	44
							45	45	45	45
							46	46	46	46
							47	47	47	47
							48	48	48	48
							49	49	49	49
							50	50	50	50
							51	51	51	51
							52	52	52	52
							53	53	53	53
							54	54	54	54
							55	55	55	55
							56	56	56	56
							57	57	57	57
							58	58	58	58
							59	59	59	59
							60	60	60	60
							61	61	61	61
							62	62	62	62
							63	63	63	63
							64	64	64	64
							65	65	65	65
							66	66	66	66
							67	67	67	67
							68	68	68	68
							69	69	69	69
							70	70	70	70
							71	71	71	71
							72	72	72	72
							73	73	73	73
							74	74	74	74
							75	75	75	75
							76	76	76	76
							77	77	77	77
							78	78	78	78
							79	79	79	79
							80	80	80	80
							81	81	81	81
							82	82	82	82
							83	83	83	83
							84	84	84	84
							85	85	85	85
							86	86	86	86
							87	87	87	87
							88	88	88	88
							89	89	89	89
							90	90	90	90
							91	91	91	91
							92	92	92	92
							93	93	93	93
							94	94	94	94
							95	95	95	95
							96	96	96	96
							97	97	97	97
							98	98	98	98
							99	99	99	99
							100	100	100	100

NOTES

PITCH COUNT TOTALS

#	PITCHER	W	L	S	IP	BF	H	R	ER	BB	SO
	TOTALS										

PITCHES BY INNING	1	2	3	4	5	6	7	8	9
TOTALS									

NOTES

FINAL SCORE		
HOME		VISITOR
	RUNS	
	HITS	
	ERRORS	
UMPIRES		
SCORER		

TEAM LINE UP

TEAM		OPPOSING TEAM	
COACH		COACH	

	NO.	STARTERS	POS.
1			
2			
3			
4			
5			
6			
7			
8			
9			
10			
11			
12			
13			
14			
15			
16			
17			

NO.	SUBSTITUTES	POS

NOTES

DATE	TIME	FIELD

TEAM LINE UP

TEAM		OPPOSING TEAM	
COACH		COACH	

	NO.	STARTERS	POS.
1			
2			
3			
4			
5			
6			
7			
8			
9			
10			
11			
12			
13			
14			
15			
16			
17			

NO.	SUBSTITUTES	POS

NOTES		
DATE	TIME	FIELD

BASEBALL / SOFTBALL SCORESHEET

	#	PLAYER	POS	1	2	3	4	5	6	7	8	9
1												
SUB.												
2												
SUB.												
3												
SUB.												
4												
SUB.												
5												
SUB.												
6												
SUB.												
7												
SUB.												
8												
SUB.												
9												
SUB.												
10												
SUB.												
11												
SUB.												
12												
SUB.												
13												
SUB.												
14												
SUB.												
15												
SUB.												
16												
SUB.												
17												
SUB.												TOTALS

INNING TOTALS	RUNS											TOTALS
	HITS											
	ERRORS											
	LEFT ON BASE											

AB	R	H	RBI	BB	SO		PLAYER #		

PLAYER # column numbers:
1, 2, 3, 4, 5, 6, 7, 8, 9, 10, 11, 12, 13, 14, 15, 16, 17, 18, 19, 20, 21, 22, 23, 24, 25, 26, 27, 28, 29, 30, 31, 32, 33, 34, 35, 36, 37, 38, 39, 40, 41, 42, 43, 44, 45, 46, 47, 48, 49, 50, 51, 52, 53, 54, 55, 56, 57, 58, 59, 60, 61, 62, 63, 64, 65, 66, 67, 68, 69, 70, 71, 72, 73, 74, 75, 76, 77, 78, 79, 80, 81, 82, 83, 84, 85, 86, 87, 88, 89, 90, 91, 92, 93, 94, 95, 96, 97, 98, 99, 100

#	PITCHER	W	L	S	IP	BF	H	R	ER	BB	SO
	TOTALS										

PITCHES BY INNING	1	2	3	4	5	6	7	8	9
TOTALS									

NOTES

FINAL SCORE

	HOME		VISITOR	
		RUNS		
		HITS		
		ERRORS		
UMPIRES				
SCORER				

NOTES

PITCH COUNT TOTALS

TEAM LINE UP

TEAM		OPPOSING TEAM	
COACH		COACH	

	NO.	STARTERS	POS.
1			
2			
3			
4			
5			
6			
7			
8			
9			
10			
11			
12			
13			
14			
15			
16			
17			

NO.	SUBSTITUTES	POS

NOTES		
DATE	TIME	FIELD

TEAM LINE UP

TEAM	OPPOSING TEAM
COACH	COACH

	NO.	STARTERS	POS.
1			
2			
3			
4			
5			
6			
7			
8			
9			
10			
11			
12			
13			
14			
15			
16			
17			

NO.	SUBSTITUTES	POS

NOTES		
DATE	TIME	FIELD

BASEBALL / SOFTBALL SCORESHEET

	#	PLAYER	POS	1	2	3	4	5	6	7	8	9
1												
SUB.												
2												
SUB.												
3												
SUB.												
4												
SUB.												
5												
SUB.												
6												
SUB.												
7												
SUB.												
8												
SUB.												
9												
SUB.												
10												
SUB.												
11												
SUB.												
12												
SUB.												
13												
SUB.												
14												
SUB.												
15												
SUB.												
16												
SUB.												
17												
SUB.												TOTALS

INNING TOTALS	RUNS									
	HITS									
	ERRORS									
	LEFT ON BASE									

AB	R	H	RBI	BB	SO	PLAYER #			
						1	1	1	1
						2	2	2	2
						3	3	3	3
						4	4	4	4
						5	5	5	5
						6	6	6	6
						7	7	7	7
						8	8	8	8
						9	9	9	9
						10	10	10	10
						11	11	11	11
						12	12	12	12
						13	13	13	13
						14	14	14	14
						15	15	15	15
						16	16	16	16
						17	17	17	17
						18	18	18	18
						19	19	19	19
						20	20	20	20
						21	21	21	21
						22	22	22	22
						23	23	23	23
						24	24	24	24
						25	25	25	25
						26	26	26	26
						27	27	27	27
						28	28	28	28
						29	29	29	29
						30	30	30	30
						31	31	31	31
						32	32	32	32
						33	33	33	33
						34	34	34	34
						35	35	35	35
						36	36	36	36
						37	37	37	37
						38	38	38	38
						39	39	39	39
						40	40	40	40
						41	41	41	41
						42	42	42	42
						43	43	43	43
						44	44	44	44
						45	45	45	45
						46	46	46	46
						47	47	47	47
						48	48	48	48
						49	49	49	49
						50	50	50	50
						51	51	51	51
						52	52	52	52
						53	53	53	53
						54	54	54	54
						55	55	55	55
						56	56	56	56
						57	57	57	57
						58	58	58	58
						59	59	59	59
						60	60	60	60
						61	61	61	61
						62	62	62	62
						63	63	63	63
						64	64	64	64
						65	65	65	65
						66	66	66	66
						67	67	67	67
						68	68	68	68
						69	69	69	69
						70	70	70	70
						71	71	71	71
						72	72	72	72
						73	73	73	73
						74	74	74	74
						75	75	75	75
						76	76	76	76
						77	77	77	77
						78	78	78	78
						79	79	79	79
						80	80	80	80
						81	81	81	81
						82	82	82	82
						83	83	83	83
						84	84	84	84
						85	85	85	85
						86	86	86	86
						87	87	87	87
						88	88	88	88
						89	89	89	89
						90	90	90	90
						91	91	91	91
						92	92	92	92
						93	93	93	93
						94	94	94	94
						95	95	95	95
						96	96	96	96
						97	97	97	97
						98	98	98	98
						99	99	99	99
						100	100	100	100

NOTES

PITCH COUNT
TOTALS

	!"#$		%o#"&#'#()$		$*!'#()$	
	+($.!					
	~-)$'					
	/(%/#.&'					

#	PITCHER	W	L	S	IP	BF	H	R	ER	BB	SO
	TOTALS										

PITCHES BY INNING	1	2	3	4	5	6	7	8	9
TOTALS									

NOTES

FINAL SCORE		
HOME		VISITOR
	RUNS	
	HITS	
	ERRORS	
UMPIRES		
SCORER		

TEAM LINE UP

TEAM	OPPOSING TEAM
COACH	COACH

	NO.	STARTERS	POS.		NO.	SUBSTITUTES	POS
1							
2							
3							
4							
5							
6							
7							
8							
9							
10							
11							
12							
13							
14							
15							
16							
17							

NOTES

DATE	TIME	FIELD

TEAM LINE UP

TEAM	OPPOSING TEAM
COACH	COACH

	NO.	STARTERS	POS.
1			
2			
3			
4			
5			
6			
7			
8			
9			
10			
11			
12			
13			
14			
15			
16			
17			

NO.	SUBSTITUTES	POS

NOTES		
DATE	TIME	FIELD

BASEBALL / SOFTBALL SCORESHEET

	#	PLAYER	POS	1	2	3	4	5	6	7	8	9
1												
SUB.												
2												
SUB.												
3												
SUB.												
4												
SUB.												
5												
SUB.												
6												
SUB.												
7												
SUB.												
8												
SUB.												
9												
SUB.												
10												
SUB.												
11												
SUB.												
12												
SUB.												
13												
SUB.												
14												
SUB.												
15												
SUB.												
16												
SUB.												
17												
SUB.												TOTALS

Each cell contains: 1B 2B 3B HR BB

INNING TOTALS	RUNS									
	HITS									
	ERRORS									
	LEFT ON BASE									

AB	R	H	RBI	BB	SO					PLAYER #
						1	1	1	1	
						2	2	2	2	
						3	3	3	3	
						4	4	4	4	
						5	5	5	5	
						6	6	6	6	
						7	7	7	7	
						8	8	8	8	
						9	9	9	9	
						10	10	10	10	
						11	11	11	11	
						12	12	12	12	
						13	13	13	13	
						14	14	14	14	
						15	15	15	15	
						16	16	16	16	
						17	17	17	17	
						18	18	18	18	
						19	19	19	19	
						20	20	20	20	
						21	21	21	21	
						22	22	22	22	
						23	23	23	23	
						24	24	24	24	
						25	25	25	25	
						26	26	26	26	
						27	27	27	27	
						28	28	28	28	
						29	29	29	29	
						30	30	30	30	
						31	31	31	31	
						32	32	32	32	
						33	33	33	33	
						34	34	34	34	
						35	35	35	35	
						36	36	36	36	
						37	37	37	37	
						38	38	38	38	
						39	39	39	39	
						40	40	40	40	
						41	41	41	41	
						42	42	42	42	
						43	43	43	43	
						44	44	44	44	
						45	45	45	45	
						46	46	46	46	
						47	47	47	47	
						48	48	48	48	
						49	49	49	49	
						50	50	50	50	
						51	51	51	51	
						52	52	52	52	
						53	53	53	53	
						54	54	54	54	
						55	55	55	55	
						56	56	56	56	
						57	57	57	57	
						58	58	58	58	
						59	59	59	59	
						60	60	60	60	
						61	61	61	61	
						62	62	62	62	
						63	63	63	63	
						64	64	64	64	
						65	65	65	65	
						66	66	66	66	
						67	67	67	67	
						68	68	68	68	
						69	69	69	69	
						70	70	70	70	
						71	71	71	71	
						72	72	72	72	
						73	73	73	73	
						74	74	74	74	
						75	75	75	75	
						76	76	76	76	
						77	77	77	77	
						78	78	78	78	
						79	79	79	79	
						80	80	80	80	
						81	81	81	81	
						82	82	82	82	
						83	83	83	83	
						84	84	84	84	
						85	85	85	85	
						86	86	86	86	
						87	87	87	87	
						88	88	88	88	
						89	89	89	89	
						90	90	90	90	
						91	91	91	91	
						92	92	92	92	
						93	93	93	93	
						94	94	94	94	
						95	95	95	95	
						96	96	96	96	
						97	97	97	97	
						98	98	98	98	
						99	99	99	99	
						100	100	100	100	

NOTES

PITCH COUNT TOTALS

#	PITCHER	W	L	S	IP	BF	H	R	ER	BB	SO
	TOTALS										

PITCHES BY INNING		1	2	3	4	5	6	7	8	9
TOTALS										

NOTES

FINAL SCORE			
HOME		VISITOR	
	RUNS		
	HITS		
	ERRORS		
UMPIRES			
SCORER			

TEAM LINE UP

TEAM		OPPOSING TEAM	
COACH		COACH	

	NO.	STARTERS	POS.		NO.	SUBSTITUTES	POS
1							
2							
3							
4							
5							
6							
7							
8							
9							
10							
11							
12							
13							
14							
15							
16							
17							

NOTES		
DATE	TIME	FIELD

TEAM LINE UP

TEAM	OPPOSING TEAM
COACH	COACH

	NO.	STARTERS	POS.
1			
2			
3			
4			
5			
6			
7			
8			
9			
10			
11			
12			
13			
14			
15			
16			
17			

NO.	SUBSTITUTES	POS

NOTES

DATE	TIME	FIELD

BASEBALL / SOFTBALL SCORESHEET

	#	PLAYER	POS	1	2	3	4	5	6	7	8	9
1												
SUB.												
2												
SUB.												
3												
SUB.												
4												
SUB.												
5												
SUB.												
6												
SUB.												
7												
SUB.												
8												
SUB.												
9												
SUB.												
10												
SUB.												
11												
SUB.												
12												
SUB.												
13												
SUB.												
14												
SUB.												
15												
SUB.												
16												
SUB.												
17												
SUB.												TOTALS

INNING TOTALS	RUNS									
	HITS									
	ERRORS									
	LEFT ON BASE									

| AB | R | H | RBI | BB | SO | PLAYER # | | | |
|----|---|---|-----|----|----| | | | |

PLAYER #

(Player number columns 1–100 repeated across four columns)

NOTES

PITCH COUNT
TOTALS

!"#$	%#"&#"#()$	$*!"#()$

+($.!

~)$'	
/(%(#.&'	

#	PITCHER	W	L	S	IP	BF	H	R	ER	BB	SO
	TOTALS										

PITCHES BY INNING	1	2	3	4	5	6	7	8	9
TOTALS									

NOTES

FINAL SCORE		
HOME		VISITOR
	RUNS	
	HITS	
	ERRORS	
UMPIRES		
SCORER		

TEAM LINE UP

TEAM		OPPOSING TEAM	
COACH		COACH	

	NO.	STARTERS	POS.
1			
2			
3			
4			
5			
6			
7			
8			
9			
10			
11			
12			
13			
14			
15			
16			
17			

NO.	SUBSTITUTES	POS

NOTES

DATE	TIME	FIELD

TEAM LINE UP

TEAM	OPPOSING TEAM
COACH	COACH

	NO.	STARTERS	POS.		NO.	SUBSTITUTES	POS
1							
2							
3							
4							
5							
6							
7							
8							
9							
10							
11							
12							
13							
14							
15							
16							
17							

NOTES

DATE	TIME	FIELD

BASEBALL / SOFTBALL SCORESHEET

	#	PLAYER	POS	1	2	3	4	5	6	7	8	9
1												
SUB.												
2												
SUB.												
3												
SUB.												
4												
SUB.												
5												
SUB.												
6												
SUB.												
7												
SUB.												
8												
SUB.												
9												
SUB.												
10												
SUB.												
11												
SUB.												
12												
SUB.												
13												
SUB.												
14												
SUB.												
15												
SUB.												
16												
SUB.												
17												
SUB.												TOTALS

INNING TOTALS	RUNS									
	HITS									
	ERRORS									
	LEFT ON BASE									

AB	R	H	RBI	BB	SO	PLAYER #			
						1	1	1	1
						2	2	2	2
						3	3	3	3
						4	4	4	4
						5	5	5	5
						6	6	6	6
						7	7	7	7
						8	8	8	8
						9	9	9	9
						10	10	10	10
						11	11	11	11
						12	12	12	12
						13	13	13	13
						14	14	14	14
						15	15	15	15
						16	16	16	16
						17	17	17	17
						18	18	18	18
						19	19	19	19
						20	20	20	20
						...	...	...	...
						100	100	100	100

NOTES

PITCH COUNT TOTALS

!"#$	%#"&#"#()$	$*!"#()$
+($.!		
-.)$'		
/(%(#.&)		

#	PITCHER	W	L	S	IP	BF	H	R	ER	BB	SO
	TOTALS										

PITCHES BY INNING	1	2	3	4	5	6	7	8	9
TOTALS									

NOTES

FINAL SCORE	
HOME	VISITOR
	RUNS	
	HITS	
	ERRORS	
UMPIRES	
SCORER	

TEAM LINE UP

TEAM		OPPOSING TEAM	
COACH		COACH	

	NO.	STARTERS	POS.
1			
2			
3			
4			
5			
6			
7			
8			
9			
10			
11			
12			
13			
14			
15			
16			
17			

NO.	SUBSTITUTES	POS

NOTES

DATE	TIME	FIELD

TEAM LINE UP

TEAM	OPPOSING TEAM
COACH	COACH

	NO.	STARTERS	POS.		NO.	SUBSTITUTES	POS
1							
2							
3							
4							
5							
6							
7							
8							
9							
10							
11							
12							
13							
14							
15							
16							
17							

NOTES		
DATE	TIME	FIELD

BASEBALL / SOFTBALL SCORESHEET

	#	PLAYER	POS	1	2	3	4	5	6	7	8	9	
1													
SUB.													
2													
SUB.													
3													
SUB.													
4													
SUB.													
5													
SUB.													
6													
SUB.													
7													
SUB.													
8													
SUB.													
9													
SUB.													
10													
SUB.													
11													
SUB.													
12													
SUB.													
13													
SUB.													
14													
SUB.													
15													
SUB.													
16													
SUB.													
17													TOTALS
SUB.													

INNING TOTALS	RUNS									
	HITS									
	ERRORS									
	LEFT ON BASE									

AB	R	H	RBI	BB	SO	PLAYER #			

PLAYER #

AB	R	H	RBI	BB	SO

(Player # columns numbered 1–100 in four columns)

1 1 1 1
2 2 2 2
3 3 3 3
4 4 4 4
5 5 5 5
6 6 6 6
7 7 7 7
8 8 8 8
9 9 9 9
10 10 10 10
11 11 11 11
12 12 12 12
13 13 13 13
14 14 14 14
15 15 15 15
16 16 16 16
17 17 17 17
18 18 18 18
19 19 19 19
20 20 20 20
21 21 21 21
22 22 22 22
23 23 23 23
24 24 24 24
25 25 25 25
26 26 26 26
27 27 27 27
28 28 28 28
29 29 29 29
30 30 30 30
31 31 31 31
32 32 32 32
33 33 33 33
34 34 34 34
35 35 35 35
36 36 36 36
37 37 37 37
38 38 38 38
39 39 39 39
40 40 40 40
41 41 41 41
42 42 42 42
43 43 43 43
44 44 44 44
45 45 45 45
46 46 46 46
47 47 47 47
48 48 48 48
49 49 49 49
50 50 50 50
51 51 51 51
52 52 52 52
53 53 53 53
54 54 54 54
55 55 55 55
56 56 56 56
57 57 57 57
58 58 58 58
59 59 59 59
60 60 60 60
61 61 61 61
62 62 62 62
63 63 63 63
64 64 64 64
65 65 65 65
66 66 66 66
67 67 67 67
68 68 68 68
69 69 69 69
70 70 70 70
71 71 71 71
72 72 72 72
73 73 73 73
74 74 74 74
75 75 75 75
76 76 76 76
77 77 77 77
78 78 78 78
79 79 79 79
80 80 80 80
81 81 81 81
82 82 82 82
83 83 83 83
84 84 84 84
85 85 85 85
86 86 86 86
87 87 87 87
88 88 88 88
89 89 89 89
90 90 90 90
91 91 91 91
92 92 92 92
93 93 93 93
94 94 94 94
95 95 95 95
96 96 96 96
97 97 97 97
98 98 98 98
99 99 99 99
100 100 100 100

NOTES

PITCH COUNT
TOTALS

!"#$ %o#"&#'#()$ $*'!#()$

+(\$.!

-.)\$'

.'(%(#.&'

#	PITCHER	W	L	S	IP	BF	H	R	ER	BB	SO
	TOTALS										

PITCHES BY INNING	1	2	3	4	5	6	7	8	9
TOTALS									

NOTES

FINAL SCORE		
HOME		VISITOR
	RUNS	
	HITS	
	ERRORS	
UMPIRES		
SCORER		

TEAM LINE UP

TEAM	OPPOSING TEAM
COACH	COACH

	NO.	STARTERS	POS.		NO.	SUBSTITUTES	POS
1							
2							
3							
4							
5							
6							
7							
8							
9							
10							
11							
12							
13							
14							
15							
16							
17							

NOTES

DATE	TIME	FIELD

TEAM LINE UP

TEAM	OPPOSING TEAM
COACH	COACH

	NO.	STARTERS	POS.
1			
2			
3			
4			
5			
6			
7			
8			
9			
10			
11			
12			
13			
14			
15			
16			
17			

NO.	SUBSTITUTES	POS

NOTES		
DATE	TIME	FIELD

BASEBALL / SOFTBALL SCORESHEET

	#	PLAYER	POS	1	2	3	4	5	6	7	8	9
1												
SUB.												
2												
SUB.												
3												
SUB.												
4												
SUB.												
5												
SUB.												
6												
SUB.												
7												
SUB.												
8												
SUB.												
9												
SUB.												
10												
SUB.												
11												
SUB.												
12												
SUB.												
13												
SUB.												
14												
SUB.												
15												
SUB.												
16												
SUB.												
17												
SUB.												TOTALS

Cell headers within each box: 1B 2B 3B HR BB

INNING TOTALS	RUNS									
	HITS									
	ERRORS									
	LEFT ON BASE									

AB	R	H	RBI	BB	SO	PLAYER #			

1	1	1	1
2	2	2	2
3	3	3	3
4	4	4	4
5	5	5	5
6	6	6	6
7	7	7	7
8	8	8	8
9	9	9	9
10	10	10	10

(Player number columns continue 1 through 100)

NOTES

PITCH COUNT TOTALS

!"#$	%#"&#"#()$	$*!#()$

+($.!

-)$'	
/(%(#.&'	

#	PITCHER	W	L	S	IP	BF	H	R	ER	BB	SO
	TOTALS										

PITCHES BY INNING	1	2	3	4	5	6	7	8	9
TOTALS									

NOTES

FINAL SCORE

HOME		VISITOR
	RUNS	
	HITS	
	ERRORS	
UMPIRES		
SCORER		

TEAM LINE UP

TEAM	OPPOSING TEAM
COACH	COACH

	NO.	STARTERS	POS.		NO.	SUBSTITUTES	POS
1							
2							
3							
4							
5							
6							
7							
8							
9							
10							
11							
12							
13							
14							
15							
16							
17							

NOTES

DATE	TIME	FIELD

TEAM LINE UP

TEAM	OPPOSING TEAM
COACH	COACH

	NO.	STARTERS	POS.		NO.	SUBSTITUTES	POS
1							
2							
3							
4							
5							
6							
7							
8							
9							
10							
11							
12							
13							
14							
15							
16							
17							

NOTES

DATE	TIME	FIELD

BASEBALL / SOFTBALL SCORESHEET

	#	PLAYER	POS	1	2	3	4	5	6	7	8	9
1												
SUB.												
2												
SUB.												
3												
SUB.												
4												
SUB.												
5												
SUB.												
6												
SUB.												
7												
SUB.												
8												
SUB.												
9												
SUB.												
10												
SUB.												
11												
SUB.												
12												
SUB.												
13												
SUB.												
14												
SUB.												
15												
SUB.												
16												
SUB.												
17												
SUB.											TOTALS

Note: each inning cell contains a baseball diamond with the labels 1B 2B 3B HR BB.

INNING TOTALS	RUNS									
	HITS									
	ERRORS									
	LEFT ON BASE									

AB	R	H	RBI	BB	SO		PLAYER #			
							1	1	1	1
							2	2	2	2
							3	3	3	3
							4	4	4	4
							5	5	5	5
							6	6	6	6
							7	7	7	7
							8	8	8	8
							9	9	9	9
							10	10	10	10
							11	11	11	11
							12	12	12	12
							13	13	13	13
							14	14	14	14
							15	15	15	15
							16	16	16	16
							17	17	17	17
							18	18	18	18
							19	19	19	19
							20	20	20	20
							21	21	21	21
							22	22	22	22
							23	23	23	23
							24	24	24	24
							25	25	25	25
							26	26	26	26
							27	27	27	27
							28	28	28	28
							29	29	29	29
							30	30	30	30
							31	31	31	31
							32	32	32	32
							33	33	33	33
							34	34	34	34
							35	35	35	35
							36	36	36	36
							37	37	37	37
							38	38	38	38
							39	39	39	39
							40	40	40	40
							41	41	41	41
							42	42	42	42
							43	43	43	43
							44	44	44	44
							45	45	45	45
							46	46	46	46
							47	47	47	47
							48	48	48	48
							49	49	49	49
							50	50	50	50
							51	51	51	51
							52	52	52	52
							53	53	53	53
							54	54	54	54
							55	55	55	55
							56	56	56	56
							57	57	57	57
							58	58	58	58
							59	59	59	59
							60	60	60	60
							61	61	61	61
							62	62	62	62
							63	63	63	63
							64	64	64	64
							65	65	65	65
							66	66	66	66
							67	67	67	67
							68	68	68	68
							69	69	69	69
							70	70	70	70
							71	71	71	71
							72	72	72	72
							73	73	73	73
							74	74	74	74
							75	75	75	75
							76	76	76	76
							77	77	77	77
							78	78	78	78
							79	79	79	79
							80	80	80	80
							81	81	81	81
							82	82	82	82
							83	83	83	83
							84	84	84	84
							85	85	85	85
							86	86	86	86
							87	87	87	87
							88	88	88	88
							89	89	89	89
							90	90	90	90
							91	91	91	91
							92	92	92	92
							93	93	93	93
							94	94	94	94
							95	95	95	95
							96	96	96	96
							97	97	97	97
							98	98	98	98
							99	99	99	99
							100	100	100	100

NOTES

PITCH COUNT TOTALS

#	PITCHER	W	L	S	IP	BF	H	R	ER	BB	SO
	TOTALS										

PITCHES BY INNING		1	2	3	4	5	6	7	8	9
TOTALS										

NOTES

FINAL SCORE

HOME			VISITOR
	RUNS		
	HITS		
	ERRORS		
UMPIRES			
SCORER			

TEAM LINE UP

TEAM	OPPOSING TEAM
COACH	COACH

	NO.	STARTERS	POS.
1			
2			
3			
4			
5			
6			
7			
8			
9			
10			
11			
12			
13			
14			
15			
16			
17			

NO.	SUBSTITUTES	POS

NOTES

DATE	TIME	FIELD

TEAM LINE UP

TEAM	OPPOSING TEAM
COACH	COACH

	NO.	STARTERS	POS.
1			
2			
3			
4			
5			
6			
7			
8			
9			
10			
11			
12			
13			
14			
15			
16			
17			

NO.	SUBSTITUTES	POS

NOTES

DATE	TIME	FIELD

BASEBALL / SOFTBALL SCORESHEET

	#	PLAYER	POS	1	2	3	4	5	6	7	8	9	
1													
SUB.													
2													
SUB.													
3													
SUB.													
4													
SUB.													
5													
SUB.													
6													
SUB.													
7													
SUB.													
8													
SUB.													
9													
SUB.													
10													
SUB.													
11													
SUB.													
12													
SUB.													
13													
SUB.													
14													
SUB.													
15													
SUB.													
16													
SUB.													
17													TOTALS
SUB.													

INNING TOTALS	RUNS									
	HITS									
	ERRORS									
	LEFT ON BASE									

AB	R	H	RBI	BB	SO		PLAYER #			

Player # columns (1–100 repeated across four columns).

!"#$ °₀#"&#'#()$ $*'!#()$

+($.!

~)$'

/(%₀#.&'

#	PITCHER	W	L	S	IP	BF	H	R	ER	BB	SO
	TOTALS										

PITCHES BY INNING	1	2	3	4	5	6	7	8	9
TOTALS									

NOTES

FINAL SCORE

	HOME			VISITOR
	RUNS			
	HITS			
	ERRORS			
UMPIRES				
SCORER				

NOTES

PITCH COUNT TOTALS

TEAM LINE UP

TEAM	OPPOSING TEAM
COACH	COACH

	NO.	STARTERS	POS.
1			
2			
3			
4			
5			
6			
7			
8			
9			
10			
11			
12			
13			
14			
15			
16			
17			

NO.	SUBSTITUTES	POS

NOTES		
DATE	TIME	FIELD

TEAM LINE UP

TEAM		OPPOSING TEAM	
COACH		COACH	

	NO.	STARTERS	POS.
1			
2			
3			
4			
5			
6			
7			
8			
9			
10			
11			
12			
13			
14			
15			
16			
17			

NO.	SUBSTITUTES	POS

NOTES

DATE	TIME	FIELD

BASEBALL / SOFTBALL SCORESHEET

	#	PLAYER	POS	1	2	3	4	5	6	7	8	9	
1													
SUB.													
2													
SUB.													
3													
SUB.													
4													
SUB.													
5													
SUB.													
6													
SUB.													
7													
SUB.													
8													
SUB.													
9													
SUB.													
10													
SUB.													
11													
SUB.													
12													
SUB.													
13													
SUB.													
14													
SUB.													
15													
SUB.													
16													
SUB.													
17													TOTALS
SUB.													

INNING TOTALS	RUNS									
	HITS									
	ERRORS									
	LEFT ON BASE									

AB	R	H	RBI	BB	SO	PLAYER #			

PLAYER #

Batting stats columns: AB, R, H, RBI, BB, SO

Pitch count numbers (four columns): 1–100

NOTES

PITCH COUNT TOTALS

#	PITCHER	W	L	S	IP	BF	H	R	ER	BB	SO
	TOTALS										

PITCHES BY INNING	1	2	3	4	5	6	7	8	9
TOTALS									

NOTES

FINAL SCORE

HOME			VISITOR
	RUNS		
	HITS		
	ERRORS		

UMPIRES	
SCORER	

TEAM LINE UP

TEAM	OPPOSING TEAM
COACH	COACH

	NO.	STARTERS	POS.
1			
2			
3			
4			
5			
6			
7			
8			
9			
10			
11			
12			
13			
14			
15			
16			
17			

NO.	SUBSTITUTES	POS

NOTES		
DATE	TIME	FIELD

TEAM LINE UP

TEAM	OPPOSING TEAM
COACH	COACH

	NO.	STARTERS	POS.
1			
2			
3			
4			
5			
6			
7			
8			
9			
10			
11			
12			
13			
14			
15			
16			
17			

NO.	SUBSTITUTES	POS

NOTES		
DATE	TIME	FIELD

BASEBALL / SOFTBALL SCORESHEET

	#	PLAYER	POS	1	2	3	4	5	6	7	8	9
1												
SUB.												
2												
SUB.												
3												
SUB.												
4												
SUB.												
5												
SUB.												
6												
SUB.												
7												
SUB.												
8												
SUB.												
9												
SUB.												
10												
SUB.												
11												
SUB.												
12												
SUB.												
13												
SUB.												
14												
SUB.												
15												
SUB.												
16												
SUB.												
17												
SUB.												TOTALS

INNING TOTALS	RUNS									
	HITS									
	ERRORS									
	LEFT ON BASE									

Note: Each inning cell contains a baseball diamond with batting outcome markers labeled "1B 2B 3B HR BB"

AB	R	H	RBI	BB	SO	PLAYER #			
						1	1	1	1
						2	2	2	2
						3	3	3	3
						4	4	4	4
						5	5	5	5
						6	6	6	6
						7	7	7	7
						8	8	8	8
						9	9	9	9
						10	10	10	10
						11	11	11	11
						12	12	12	12
						13	13	13	13
						14	14	14	14
						15	15	15	15
						16	16	16	16
						17	17	17	17
						18	18	18	18
						19	19	19	19
						20	20	20	20
						21	21	21	21
						22	22	22	22
						23	23	23	23
						24	24	24	24
						25	25	25	25
						26	26	26	26
						27	27	27	27
						28	28	28	28
						29	29	29	29
						30	30	30	30
						31	31	31	31
						32	32	32	32
						33	33	33	33
						34	34	34	34
						35	35	35	35
						36	36	36	36
						37	37	37	37
						38	38	38	38
						39	39	39	39
						40	40	40	40
						41	41	41	41
						42	42	42	42
						43	43	43	43
						44	44	44	44
						45	45	45	45
						46	46	46	46
						47	47	47	47
						48	48	48	48
						49	49	49	49
						50	50	50	50
						51	51	51	51
						52	52	52	52
						53	53	53	53
						54	54	54	54
						55	55	55	55
						56	56	56	56
						57	57	57	57
						58	58	58	58
						59	59	59	59
						60	60	60	60
						61	61	61	61
						62	62	62	62
						63	63	63	63
						64	64	64	64
						65	65	65	65
						66	66	66	66
						67	67	67	67
						68	68	68	68
						69	69	69	69
						70	70	70	70
						71	71	71	71
						72	72	72	72
						73	73	73	73
						74	74	74	74
						75	75	75	75
						76	76	76	76
						77	77	77	77
						78	78	78	78
						79	79	79	79
						80	80	80	80
						81	81	81	81
						82	82	82	82
						83	83	83	83
						84	84	84	84
						85	85	85	85
						86	86	86	86
						87	87	87	87
						88	88	88	88
						89	89	89	89
						90	90	90	90
						91	91	91	91
						92	92	92	92
						93	93	93	93
						94	94	94	94
						95	95	95	95
						96	96	96	96
						97	97	97	97
						98	98	98	98
						99	99	99	99
						100	100	100	100

NOTES

PITCH COUNT TOTALS

#	PITCHER	W	L	S	IP	BF	H	R	ER	BB	SO
	TOTALS										

PITCHES BY INNING	1	2	3	4	5	6	7	8	9
TOTALS									

NOTES

FINAL SCORE	
HOME	VISITOR
	RUNS	
	HITS	
	ERRORS	
UMPIRES	
SCORER	

TEAM LINE UP

TEAM	OPPOSING TEAM
COACH	COACH

	NO.	STARTERS	POS.
1			
2			
3			
4			
5			
6			
7			
8			
9			
10			
11			
12			
13			
14			
15			
16			
17			

NO.	SUBSTITUTES	POS

NOTES		
DATE	TIME	FIELD

TEAM LINE UP

TEAM	OPPOSING TEAM
COACH	COACH

	NO.	STARTERS	POS.
1			
2			
3			
4			
5			
6			
7			
8			
9			
10			
11			
12			
13			
14			
15			
16			
17			

NO.	SUBSTITUTES	POS

NOTES		
DATE	TIME	FIELD

BASEBALL / SOFTBALL SCORESHEET

	#	PLAYER	POS	1	2	3	4	5	6	7	8	9
1												
SUB.												
2												
SUB.												
3												
SUB.												
4												
SUB.												
5												
SUB.												
6												
SUB.												
7												
SUB.												
8												
SUB.												
9												
SUB.												
10												
SUB.												
11												
SUB.												
12												
SUB.												
13												
SUB.												
14												
SUB.												
15												
SUB.												
16												
SUB.												
17												
SUB.												TOTALS

Each inning cell contains: 1B 2B 3B HR BB with a diamond diagram.

INNING TOTALS	RUNS									
	HITS									
	ERRORS									
	LEFT ON BASE									

AB	R	H	RBI	BB	SO	PLAYER #			

PLAYER #

Player count columns (1–100) appear four times across.

!"#$	%o#"&#"#()$	S*!"#()$
+($.!		

-)$'	
/(%d#.&'	

#	PITCHER	W	L	S	IP	BF	H	R	ER	BB	SO
	TOTALS										

PITCHES BY INNING	1	2	3	4	5	6	7	8	9
TOTALS									

NOTES

FINAL SCORE	
HOME	VISITOR
RUNS	
HITS	
ERRORS	
UMPIRES	
SCORER	

NOTES

PITCH COUNT
TOTALS

TEAM LINE UP

TEAM		OPPOSING TEAM	
COACH		COACH	

	NO.	STARTERS	POS.
1			
2			
3			
4			
5			
6			
7			
8			
9			
10			
11			
12			
13			
14			
15			
16			
17			

NO.	SUBSTITUTES	POS

NOTES

DATE	TIME	FIELD

TEAM LINE UP

TEAM	OPPOSING TEAM
COACH	COACH

	NO.	STARTERS	POS.
1			
2			
3			
4			
5			
6			
7			
8			
9			
10			
11			
12			
13			
14			
15			
16			
17			

NO.	SUBSTITUTES	POS

NOTES		
DATE	TIME	FIELD

BASEBALL / SOFTBALL SCORESHEET

	#	PLAYER	POS	1	2	3	4	5	6	7	8	9
1												
SUB.												
2												
SUB.												
3												
SUB.												
4												
SUB.												
5												
SUB.												
6												
SUB.												
7												
SUB.												
8												
SUB.												
9												
SUB.												
10												
SUB.												
11												
SUB.												
12												
SUB.												
13												
SUB.												
14												
SUB.												
15												
SUB.												
16												
SUB.												
17												
SUB.											TOTALS

INNING TOTALS	RUNS									
	HITS									
	ERRORS									
	LEFT ON BASE									

Each at-bat cell contains: 1B 2B 3B HR BB with a baseball diamond diagram.

AB	R	H	RBI	BB	SO	PLAYER #			

PLAYER #

Player number columns 1-100 (four columns each numbered 1 through 100)

NOTES

PITCH COUNT TOTALS

!"#$ %#"&#'#()$ $*!'#()$

+($.!

-.)$'

/(%(#.&'

#	PITCHER	W	L	S	IP	BF	H	R	ER	BB	SO
	TOTALS										

PITCHES BY INNING	1	2	3	4	5	6	7	8	9
TOTALS									

NOTES

FINAL SCORE

	HOME		VISITOR
	RUNS		
	HITS		
	ERRORS		
UMPIRES			
SCORER			

TEAM LINE UP

TEAM	OPPOSING TEAM
COACH	COACH

	NO.	STARTERS	POS.		NO.	SUBSTITUTES	POS
1							
2							
3							
4							
5							
6							
7							
8							
9							
10							
11							
12							
13							
14							
15							
16							
17							

NOTES		
DATE	TIME	FIELD

TEAM LINE UP

TEAM		OPPOSING TEAM	
COACH		COACH	

	NO.	STARTERS	POS.
1			
2			
3			
4			
5			
6			
7			
8			
9			
10			
11			
12			
13			
14			
15			
16			
17			

NO.	SUBSTITUTES	POS

NOTES		
DATE	TIME	FIELD

BASEBALL / SOFTBALL SCORESHEET

	#	PLAYER	POS	1	2	3	4	5	6	7	8	9
1												
SUB.												
2												
SUB.												
3												
SUB.												
4												
SUB.												
5												
SUB.												
6												
SUB.												
7												
SUB.												
8												
SUB.												
9												
SUB.												
10												
SUB.												
11												
SUB.												
12												
SUB.												
13												
SUB.												
14												
SUB.												
15												
SUB.												
16												
SUB.												
17												
SUB.												TOTALS

INNING TOTALS	RUNS									
	HITS									
	ERRORS									
	LEFT ON BASE									

AB	R	H	RBI	BB	SO	PLAYER #			
						1 1 1 1
						2 2 2 2
						3 3 3 3
						4 4 4 4
						5 5 5 5
						6 6 6 6
						7 7 7 7
						8 8 8 8
						9 9 9 9
						10 10 10 10
						11 11 11 11
						12 12 12 12
						13 13 13 13
						14 14 14 14
						15 15 15 15
						16 16 16 16
						17 17 17 17
						18 18 18 18
						19 19 19 19
						20 20 20 20
						...
						100 100 100 100

NOTES

PITCH COUNT
TOTALS

#	PITCHER	W	L	S	IP	BF	H	R	ER	BB	SO
	TOTALS										

PITCHES BY INNING	1	2	3	4	5	6	7	8	9
TOTALS									

NOTES

FINAL SCORE		
HOME		VISITOR
	RUNS	
	HITS	
	ERRORS	
UMPIRES		
SCORER		

TEAM LINE UP

TEAM	OPPOSING TEAM
COACH	COACH

	NO.	STARTERS	POS.
1			
2			
3			
4			
5			
6			
7			
8			
9			
10			
11			
12			
13			
14			
15			
16			
17			

NO.	SUBSTITUTES	POS

NOTES		
DATE	TIME	FIELD

TEAM LINE UP

TEAM		OPPOSING TEAM	
COACH		COACH	

	NO.	STARTERS	POS.		NO.	SUBSTITUTES	POS
1							
2							
3							
4							
5							
6							
7							
8							
9							
10							
11							
12							
13							
14							
15							
16							
17							

NOTES		
DATE	TIME	FIELD

BASEBALL / SOFTBALL SCORESHEET

	#	PLAYER	POS	1	2	3	4	5	6	7	8	9
1												
SUB.												
2												
SUB.												
3												
SUB.												
4												
SUB.												
5												
SUB.												
6												
SUB.												
7												
SUB.												
8												
SUB.												
9												
SUB.												
10												
SUB.												
11												
SUB.												
12												
SUB.												
13												
SUB.												
14												
SUB.												
15												
SUB.												
16												
SUB.												
17												
SUB.												TOTALS

INNING TOTALS	RUNS									
	HITS									
	ERRORS									
	LEFT ON BASE									

Each batter cell is labeled: 1B 2B 3B HR BB

AB	R	H	RBI	BB	SO	PLAYER #			
						1	1	1	1
						2	2	2	2
						3	3	3	3
						4	4	4	4
						5	5	5	5
						6	6	6	6
						7	7	7	7
						8	8	8	8
						9	9	9	9
						10	10	10	10
						11	11	11	11
						12	12	12	12
						13	13	13	13
						14	14	14	14
						15	15	15	15
						16	16	16	16
						17	17	17	17
						18	18	18	18
						19	19	19	19
						20	20	20	20
						21	21	21	21
						22	22	22	22
						23	23	23	23
						24	24	24	24
						25	25	25	25
						26	26	26	26
						27	27	27	27
						28	28	28	28
						29	29	29	29
						30	30	30	30
						31	31	31	31
						32	32	32	32
						33	33	33	33
						34	34	34	34
						35	35	35	35
						36	36	36	36
						37	37	37	37
						38	38	38	38
						39	39	39	39
						40	40	40	40
						41	41	41	41
						42	42	42	42
						43	43	43	43
						44	44	44	44
						45	45	45	45
						46	46	46	46
						47	47	47	47
						48	48	48	48
						49	49	49	49
						50	50	50	50
						51	51	51	51
						52	52	52	52
						53	53	53	53
						54	54	54	54
						55	55	55	55
						56	56	56	56
						57	57	57	57
						58	58	58	58
						59	59	59	59
						60	60	60	60
						61	61	61	61
						62	62	62	62
						63	63	63	63
						64	64	64	64
						65	65	65	65
						66	66	66	66
						67	67	67	67
						68	68	68	68
						69	69	69	69
						70	70	70	70
						71	71	71	71
						72	72	72	72
						73	73	73	73
						74	74	74	74
						75	75	75	75
						76	76	76	76
						77	77	77	77
						78	78	78	78
						79	79	79	79
						80	80	80	80
						81	81	81	81
						82	82	82	82
						83	83	83	83
						84	84	84	84
						85	85	85	85
						86	86	86	86
						87	87	87	87
						88	88	88	88
						89	89	89	89
						90	90	90	90
						91	91	91	91
						92	92	92	92
						93	93	93	93
						94	94	94	94
						95	95	95	95
						96	96	96	96
						97	97	97	97
						98	98	98	98
						99	99	99	99
						100	100	100	100

NOTES

PITCH COUNT TOTALS

!"#$	%#"&#$#()$	$*!"#()$
+($.!		
~)$'		
/(%(#.&'		

#	PITCHER	W	L	S	IP	BF	H	R	ER	BB	SO
	TOTALS										

PITCHES BY INNING	1	2	3	4	5	6	7	8	9
TOTALS									

NOTES

FINAL SCORE

HOME		VISITOR
	RUNS	
	HITS	
	ERRORS	
UMPIRES		
SCORER		

TEAM LINE UP

TEAM	OPPOSING TEAM
COACH	COACH

	NO.	STARTERS	POS.
1			
2			
3			
4			
5			
6			
7			
8			
9			
10			
11			
12			
13			
14			
15			
16			
17			

NO.	SUBSTITUTES	POS

NOTES		
DATE	TIME	FIELD

TEAM LINE UP

TEAM	OPPOSING TEAM
COACH	COACH

	NO.	STARTERS	POS.		NO.	SUBSTITUTES	POS
1							
2							
3							
4							
5							
6							
7							
8							
9							
10							
11							
12							
13							
14							
15							
16							
17							

NOTES

DATE	TIME	FIELD

BASEBALL / SOFTBALL SCORESHEET

	#	PLAYER	POS	1	2	3	4	5	6	7	8	9	
1													
SUB.													
2													
SUB.													
3													
SUB.													
4													
SUB.													
5													
SUB.													
6													
SUB.													
7													
SUB.													
8													
SUB.													
9													
SUB.													
10													
SUB.													
11													
SUB.													
12													
SUB.													
13													
SUB.													
14													
SUB.													
15													
SUB.													
16													
SUB.													
17													
SUB.												TOTALS

INNING TOTALS	RUNS									
	HITS									
	ERRORS									
	LEFT ON BASE									

AB	R	H	RBI	BB	SO	PLAYER #			
						1	1	1	1
						2	2	2	2
						3	3	3	3
						4	4	4	4
						5	5	5	5
						6	6	6	6
						7	7	7	7
						8	8	8	8
						9	9	9	9
						10	10	10	10
						11	11	11	11
						12	12	12	12
						13	13	13	13
						14	14	14	14
						15	15	15	15
						16	16	16	16
						17	17	17	17
						18	18	18	18
						19	19	19	19
						20	20	20	20
						21	21	21	21
						22	22	22	22
						23	23	23	23
						24	24	24	24
						25	25	25	25
						26	26	26	26
						27	27	27	27
						28	28	28	28
						29	29	29	29
						30	30	30	30
						31	31	31	31
						32	32	32	32
						33	33	33	33
						34	34	34	34
						35	35	35	35
						36	36	36	36
						37	37	37	37
						38	38	38	38
						39	39	39	39
						40	40	40	40
						41	41	41	41
						42	42	42	42
						43	43	43	43
						44	44	44	44
						45	45	45	45
						46	46	46	46
						47	47	47	47
						48	48	48	48
						49	49	49	49
						50	50	50	50
						51	51	51	51
						52	52	52	52
						53	53	53	53
						54	54	54	54
						55	55	55	55
						56	56	56	56
						57	57	57	57
						58	58	58	58
						59	59	59	59
						60	60	60	60
						61	61	61	61
						62	62	62	62
						63	63	63	63
						64	64	64	64
						65	65	65	65
						66	66	66	66
						67	67	67	67
						68	68	68	68
						69	69	69	69
						70	70	70	70
						71	71	71	71
						72	72	72	72
						73	73	73	73
						74	74	74	74
						75	75	75	75
						76	76	76	76
						77	77	77	77
						78	78	78	78
						79	79	79	79
						80	80	80	80
						81	81	81	81
						82	82	82	82
						83	83	83	83
						84	84	84	84
						85	85	85	85
						86	86	86	86
						87	87	87	87
						88	88	88	88
						89	89	89	89
						90	90	90	90
						91	91	91	91
						92	92	92	92
						93	93	93	93
						94	94	94	94
						95	95	95	95
						96	96	96	96
						97	97	97	97
						98	98	98	98
						99	99	99	99
						100	100	100	100

NOTES

PITCH COUNT
TOTALS

#	PITCHER	W	L	S	IP	BF	H	R	ER	BB	SO
	TOTALS										

PITCHES BY INNING	1	2	3	4	5	6	7	8	9
TOTALS									

NOTES

FINAL SCORE

HOME		VISITOR
	RUNS	
	HITS	
	ERRORS	
UMPIRES		
SCORER		

TEAM LINE UP

TEAM	OPPOSING TEAM
COACH	COACH

	NO.	STARTERS	POS.		NO.	SUBSTITUTES	POS
1							
2							
3							
4							
5							
6							
7							
8							
9							
10							
11							
12							
13							
14							
15							
16							
17							

NOTES

DATE	TIME	FIELD

TEAM LINE UP

TEAM	OPPOSING TEAM
COACH	COACH

	NO.	STARTERS	POS.
1			
2			
3			
4			
5			
6			
7			
8			
9			
10			
11			
12			
13			
14			
15			
16			
17			

NO.	SUBSTITUTES	POS

NOTES

DATE	TIME	FIELD

BASEBALL / SOFTBALL SCORESHEET

	#	PLAYER	POS	1	2	3	4	5	6	7	8	9
1												
SUB.												
2												
SUB.												
3												
SUB.												
4												
SUB.												
5												
SUB.												
6												
SUB.												
7												
SUB.												
8												
SUB.												
9												
SUB.												
10												
SUB.												
11												
SUB.												
12												
SUB.												
13												
SUB.												
14												
SUB.												
15												
SUB.												
16												
SUB.												
17												TOTALS
SUB.												

INNING TOTALS		
	RUNS	
	HITS	
	ERRORS	
	LEFT ON BASE	

Each inning cell shows: 1B 2B 3B HR BB

AB	R	H	RBI	BB	SO		PLAYER #		

PLAYER #

1	1	1	1
2	2	2	2
3	3	3	3
4	4	4	4
5	5	5	5
6	6	6	6
7	7	7	7
8	8	8	8
9	9	9	9
10	10	10	10
11	11	11	11
12	12	12	12
13	13	13	13
14	14	14	14
15	15	15	15
16	16	16	16
17	17	17	17
18	18	18	18
19	19	19	19
20	20	20	20
21	21	21	21
22	22	22	22
23	23	23	23
24	24	24	24
25	25	25	25
26	26	26	26
27	27	27	27
28	28	28	28
29	29	29	29
30	30	30	30
31	31	31	31
32	32	32	32
33	33	33	33
34	34	34	34
35	35	35	35
36	36	36	36
37	37	37	37
38	38	38	38
39	39	39	39
40	40	40	40
41	41	41	41
42	42	42	42
43	43	43	43
44	44	44	44
45	45	45	45
46	46	46	46
47	47	47	47
48	48	48	48
49	49	49	49
50	50	50	50
51	51	51	51
52	52	52	52
53	53	53	53
54	54	54	54
55	55	55	55
56	56	56	56
57	57	57	57
58	58	58	58
59	59	59	59
60	60	60	60
61	61	61	61
62	62	62	62
63	63	63	63
64	64	64	64
65	65	65	65
66	66	66	66
67	67	67	67
68	68	68	68
69	69	69	69
70	70	70	70
71	71	71	71
72	72	72	72
73	73	73	73
74	74	74	74
75	75	75	75
76	76	76	76
77	77	77	77
78	78	78	78
79	79	79	79
80	80	80	80
81	81	81	81
82	82	82	82
83	83	83	83
84	84	84	84
85	85	85	85
86	86	86	86
87	87	87	87
88	88	88	88
89	89	89	89
90	90	90	90
91	91	91	91
92	92	92	92
93	93	93	93
94	94	94	94
95	95	95	95
96	96	96	96
97	97	97	97
98	98	98	98
99	99	99	99
100	100	100	100

NOTES

PITCH COUNT
TOTALS

!"#$ %o#"&#'#()$ $*'!'#()$

+($.!

-.)$'

/(%o(#.&'

#	PITCHER	W	L	S	IP	BF	H	R	ER	BB	SO
	TOTALS										

PITCHES BY INNING	1	2	3	4	5	6	7	8	9
TOTALS									

NOTES

FINAL SCORE

HOME		VISITOR
	RUNS	
	HITS	
	ERRORS	

UMPIRES	
SCORER	

TEAM LINE UP

TEAM	OPPOSING TEAM
COACH	COACH

	NO.	STARTERS	POS.
1			
2			
3			
4			
5			
6			
7			
8			
9			
10			
11			
12			
13			
14			
15			
16			
17			

NO.	SUBSTITUTES	POS

NOTES

DATE	TIME	FIELD

TEAM LINE UP

TEAM	OPPOSING TEAM
COACH	COACH

	NO.	STARTERS	POS.		NO.	SUBSTITUTES	POS
1							
2							
3							
4							
5							
6							
7							
8							
9							
10							
11							
12							
13							
14							
15							
16							
17							

NOTES		
DATE	TIME	FIELD

BASEBALL / SOFTBALL SCORESHEET

	#	PLAYER	POS	1	2	3	4	5	6	7	8	9	
1				1B 2B 3B HR BB		1B 2B 3B HR BB		1B 2B 3B HR BB		1B 2B 3B HR BB		1B 2B 3B HR BB	
SUB.													
2				1B 2B 3B HR BB		1B 2B 3B HR BB		1B 2B 3B HR BB		1B 2B 3B HR BB		1B 2B 3B HR BB	
SUB.													
3				1B 2B 3B HR BB		1B 2B 3B HR BB		1B 2B 3B HR BB		1B 2B 3B HR BB		1B 2B 3B HR BB	
SUB.													
4				1B 2B 3B HR BB		1B 2B 3B HR BB		1B 2B 3B HR BB		1B 2B 3B HR BB		1B 2B 3B HR BB	
SUB.													
5				1B 2B 3B HR BB		1B 2B 3B HR BB		1B 2B 3B HR BB		1B 2B 3B HR BB		1B 2B 3B HR BB	
SUB.													
6				1B 2B 3B HR BB		1B 2B 3B HR BB		1B 2B 3B HR BB		1B 2B 3B HR BB		1B 2B 3B HR BB	
SUB.													
7				1B 2B 3B HR BB		1B 2B 3B HR BB		1B 2B 3B HR BB		1B 2B 3B HR BB		1B 2B 3B HR BB	
SUB.													
8				1B 2B 3B HR BB		1B 2B 3B HR BB		1B 2B 3B HR BB		1B 2B 3B HR BB		1B 2B 3B HR BB	
SUB.													
9				1B 2B 3B HR BB		1B 2B 3B HR BB		1B 2B 3B HR BB		1B 2B 3B HR BB		1B 2B 3B HR BB	
SUB.													
10				1B 2B 3B HR BB		1B 2B 3B HR BB		1B 2B 3B HR BB		1B 2B 3B HR BB		1B 2B 3B HR BB	
SUB.													
11				1B 2B 3B HR BB		1B 2B 3B HR BB		1B 2B 3B HR BB		1B 2B 3B HR BB		1B 2B 3B HR BB	
SUB.													
12				1B 2B 3B HR BB		1B 2B 3B HR BB		1B 2B 3B HR BB		1B 2B 3B HR BB		1B 2B 3B HR BB	
SUB.													
13				1B 2B 3B HR BB		1B 2B 3B HR BB		1B 2B 3B HR BB		1B 2B 3B HR BB		1B 2B 3B HR BB	
SUB.													
14				1B 2B 3B HR BB		1B 2B 3B HR BB		1B 2B 3B HR BB		1B 2B 3B HR BB		1B 2B 3B HR BB	
SUB.													
15				1B 2B 3B HR BB		1B 2B 3B HR BB		1B 2B 3B HR BB		1B 2B 3B HR BB		1B 2B 3B HR BB	
SUB.													
16				1B 2B 3B HR BB		1B 2B 3B HR BB		1B 2B 3B HR BB		1B 2B 3B HR BB		1B 2B 3B HR BB	
SUB.													
17				1B 2B 3B HR BB		1B 2B 3B HR BB		1B 2B 3B HR BB		1B 2B 3B HR BB		1B 2B 3B HR BB	
SUB.													TOTALS

INNING TOTALS	RUNS										
	HITS										
	ERRORS										
	LEFT ON BASE										

AB	R	H	RBI	BB	SO					PLAYER #

Player # columns (1–100) repeated across four columns:

1–100 (each of four columns lists 1 through 100)

NOTES

PITCH COUNT TOTALS

!"#$ %#"&#'#()$ $*!'#()$
+($.!
-.)$'
/(%(#.&'

#	PITCHER	W	L	S	IP	BF	H	R	ER	BB	SO
	TOTALS										

PITCHES BY INNING		1	2	3	4	5	6	7	8	9
	TOTALS										

NOTES

FINAL SCORE	
HOME	VISITOR
RUNS	
HITS	
ERRORS	

UMPIRES	
SCORER	

TEAM LINE UP

TEAM	OPPOSING TEAM
COACH	COACH

	NO.	STARTERS	POS.
1			
2			
3			
4			
5			
6			
7			
8			
9			
10			
11			
12			
13			
14			
15			
16			
17			

NO.	SUBSTITUTES	POS

NOTES

DATE	TIME	FIELD

TEAM LINE UP

TEAM		OPPOSING TEAM	
COACH		COACH	

	NO.	STARTERS	POS.
1			
2			
3			
4			
5			
6			
7			
8			
9			
10			
11			
12			
13			
14			
15			
16			
17			

NO.	SUBSTITUTES	POS

NOTES

DATE	TIME	FIELD

BASEBALL / SOFTBALL SCORESHEET

	#	PLAYER	POS	1	2	3	4	5	6	7	8	9
1				1B 2B 3B HR BB		1B 2B 3B HR BB		1B 2B 3B HR BB		1B 2B 3B HR BB		1B 2B 3B HR BB
SUB.												
2				1B 2B 3B HR BB		1B 2B 3B HR BB		1B 2B 3B HR BB		1B 2B 3B HR BB		1B 2B 3B HR BB
SUB.												
3				1B 2B 3B HR BB		1B 2B 3B HR BB		1B 2B 3B HR BB		1B 2B 3B HR BB		1B 2B 3B HR BB
SUB.												
4				1B 2B 3B HR BB		1B 2B 3B HR BB		1B 2B 3B HR BB		1B 2B 3B HR BB		1B 2B 3B HR BB
SUB.												
5				1B 2B 3B HR BB		1B 2B 3B HR BB		1B 2B 3B HR BB		1B 2B 3B HR BB		1B 2B 3B HR BB
SUB.												
6				1B 2B 3B HR BB		1B 2B 3B HR BB		1B 2B 3B HR BB		1B 2B 3B HR BB		1B 2B 3B HR BB
SUB.												
7				1B 2B 3B HR BB		1B 2B 3B HR BB		1B 2B 3B HR BB		1B 2B 3B HR BB		1B 2B 3B HR BB
SUB.												
8				1B 2B 3B HR BB		1B 2B 3B HR BB		1B 2B 3B HR BB		1B 2B 3B HR BB		1B 2B 3B HR BB
SUB.												
9				1B 2B 3B HR BB		1B 2B 3B HR BB		1B 2B 3B HR BB		1B 2B 3B HR BB		1B 2B 3B HR BB
SUB.												
10				1B 2B 3B HR BB		1B 2B 3B HR BB		1B 2B 3B HR BB		1B 2B 3B HR BB		1B 2B 3B HR BB
SUB.												
11				1B 2B 3B HR BB		1B 2B 3B HR BB		1B 2B 3B HR BB		1B 2B 3B HR BB		1B 2B 3B HR BB
SUB.												
12				1B 2B 3B HR BB		1B 2B 3B HR BB		1B 2B 3B HR BB		1B 2B 3B HR BB		1B 2B 3B HR BB
SUB.												
13				1B 2B 3B HR BB		1B 2B 3B HR BB		1B 2B 3B HR BB		1B 2B 3B HR BB		1B 2B 3B HR BB
SUB.												
14				1B 2B 3B HR BB		1B 2B 3B HR BB		1B 2B 3B HR BB		1B 2B 3B HR BB		1B 2B 3B HR BB
SUB.												
15				1B 2B 3B HR BB		1B 2B 3B HR BB		1B 2B 3B HR BB		1B 2B 3B HR BB		1B 2B 3B HR BB
SUB.												
16				1B 2B 3B HR BB		1B 2B 3B HR BB		1B 2B 3B HR BB		1B 2B 3B HR BB		1B 2B 3B HR BB
SUB.												
17				1B 2B 3B HR BB		1B 2B 3B HR BB		1B 2B 3B HR BB		1B 2B 3B HR BB		1B 2B 3B HR BB
SUB.													TOTALS

INNING TOTALS		RUNS											
		HITS											
		ERRORS											
		LEFT ON BASE											

AB	R	H	RBI	BB	SO			PLAYER #		

PLAYER #

Number columns listing 1–100 repeated across four sub-columns.

#	PITCHER	W	L	S	IP	BF	H	R	ER	BB	SO
	TOTALS										

PITCHES BY INNING	1	2	3	4	5	6	7	8	9
TOTALS									

NOTES

FINAL SCORE

HOME		VISITOR
	RUNS	
	HITS	
	ERRORS	

UMPIRES	
SCORER	

NOTES

PITCH COUNT
TOTALS

AB	R	H	RBI	BB	SO

TEAM LINE UP

TEAM	OPPOSING TEAM
COACH	COACH

	NO.	STARTERS	POS.
1			
2			
3			
4			
5			
6			
7			
8			
9			
10			
11			
12			
13			
14			
15			
16			
17			

NO.	SUBSTITUTES	POS

NOTES		
DATE	TIME	FIELD

TEAM LINE UP

TEAM	OPPOSING TEAM
COACH	COACH

	NO.	STARTERS	POS.		NO.	SUBSTITUTES	POS
1							
2							
3							
4							
5							
6							
7							
8							
9							
10							
11							
12							
13							
14							
15							
16							
17							

NOTES		
DATE	TIME	FIELD

BASEBALL / SOFTBALL SCORESHEET

	#	PLAYER	POS	1	2	3	4	5	6	7	8	9	
1													
SUB.													
2													
SUB.													
3													
SUB.													
4													
SUB.													
5													
SUB.													
6													
SUB.													
7													
SUB.													
8													
SUB.													
9													
SUB.													
10													
SUB.													
11													
SUB.													
12													
SUB.													
13													
SUB.													
14													
SUB.													
15													
SUB.													
16													
SUB.													
17													
SUB.													TOTALS

INNING TOTALS	RUNS									
	HITS									
	ERRORS									
	LEFT ON BASE									

AB	R	H	RBI	BB	SO		PLAYER #			
							1	1	1	1
							2	2	2	2
							3	3	3	3
							4	4	4	4
							5	5	5	5
							6	6	6	6
							7	7	7	7
							8	8	8	8
							9	9	9	9
							10	10	10	10

(Player # column continues numbering 1–100 in four columns.)

#	PITCHER	W	L	S	IP	BF	H	R	ER	BB	SO
	TOTALS										

PITCHES BY INNING	1	2	3	4	5	6	7	8	9
TOTALS									

NOTES

(blank lines)

FINAL SCORE

HOME			VISITOR
	RUNS		
	HITS		
	ERRORS		
UMPIRES			
SCORER			

NOTES

PITCH COUNT
TOTALS

TEAM LINE UP

TEAM		OPPOSING TEAM	
COACH		COACH	

	NO.	STARTERS	POS.
1			
2			
3			
4			
5			
6			
7			
8			
9			
10			
11			
12			
13			
14			
15			
16			
17			

NO.	SUBSTITUTES	POS

NOTES		
DATE	TIME	FIELD

TEAM LINE UP

TEAM	OPPOSING TEAM
COACH	COACH

	NO.	STARTERS	POS.
1			
2			
3			
4			
5			
6			
7			
8			
9			
10			
11			
12			
13			
14			
15			
16			
17			

NO.	SUBSTITUTES	POS

NOTES

DATE	TIME	FIELD

BASEBALL / SOFTBALL SCORESHEET

	#	PLAYER	POS	1	2	3	4	5	6	7	8	9
1												
SUB.												
2												
SUB.												
3												
SUB.												
4												
SUB.												
5												
SUB.												
6												
SUB.												
7												
SUB.												
8												
SUB.												
9												
SUB.												
10												
SUB.												
11												
SUB.												
12												
SUB.												
13												
SUB.												
14												
SUB.												
15												
SUB.												
16												
SUB.												
17												TOTALS
SUB.												

INNING TOTALS	RUNS									
	HITS									
	ERRORS									
	LEFT ON BASE									

Each batting cell contains the notation: 1B 2B 3B HR BB

AB	R	H	RBI	BB	SO	PLAYER #			

PLAYER #			
1	1	1	1
2	2	2	2
3	3	3	3
4	4	4	4
5	5	5	5
6	6	6	6
7	7	7	7
8	8	8	8
9	9	9	9
10	10	10	10
11	11	11	11
12	12	12	12
13	13	13	13
14	14	14	14
15	15	15	15
16	16	16	16
17	17	17	17
18	18	18	18
19	19	19	19
20	20	20	20
21	21	21	21
22	22	22	22
23	23	23	23
24	24	24	24
25	25	25	25
26	26	26	26
27	27	27	27
28	28	28	28
29	29	29	29
30	30	30	30
31	31	31	31
32	32	32	32
33	33	33	33
34	34	34	34
35	35	35	35
36	36	36	36
37	37	37	37
38	38	38	38
39	39	39	39
40	40	40	40
41	41	41	41
42	42	42	42
43	43	43	43
44	44	44	44
45	45	45	45
46	46	46	46
47	47	47	47
48	48	48	48
49	49	49	49
50	50	50	50
51	51	51	51
52	52	52	52
53	53	53	53
54	54	54	54
55	55	55	55
56	56	56	56
57	57	57	57
58	58	58	58
59	59	59	59
60	60	60	60
61	61	61	61
62	62	62	62
63	63	63	63
64	64	64	64
65	65	65	65
66	66	66	66
67	67	67	67
68	68	68	68
69	69	69	69
70	70	70	70
71	71	71	71
72	72	72	72
73	73	73	73
74	74	74	74
75	75	75	75
76	76	76	76
77	77	77	77
78	78	78	78
79	79	79	79
80	80	80	80
81	81	81	81
82	82	82	82
83	83	83	83
84	84	84	84
85	85	85	85
86	86	86	86
87	87	87	87
88	88	88	88
89	89	89	89
90	90	90	90
91	91	91	91
92	92	92	92
93	93	93	93
94	94	94	94
95	95	95	95
96	96	96	96
97	97	97	97
98	98	98	98
99	99	99	99
100	100	100	100

NOTES

PITCH COUNT TOTALS

#	PITCHER	W	L	S	IP	BF	H	R	ER	BB	SO
	TOTALS										

PITCHES BY INNING	1	2	3	4	5	6	7	8	9
TOTALS									

NOTES

FINAL SCORE

HOME		VISITOR
	RUNS	
	HITS	
	ERRORS	

UMPIRES	
SCORER	

TEAM LINE UP

TEAM	OPPOSING TEAM
COACH	COACH

	NO.	STARTERS	POS.
1			
2			
3			
4			
5			
6			
7			
8			
9			
10			
11			
12			
13			
14			
15			
16			
17			

NO.	SUBSTITUTES	POS

NOTES

DATE	TIME	FIELD

TEAM LINE UP

TEAM	OPPOSING TEAM
COACH	COACH

	NO.	STARTERS	POS.		NO.	SUBSTITUTES	POS
1							
2							
3							
4							
5							
6							
7							
8							
9							
10							
11							
12							
13							
14							
15							
16							
17							

NOTES

DATE	TIME	FIELD

BASEBALL / SOFTBALL SCORESHEET

	#	PLAYER	POS	1	2	3	4	5	6	7	8	9
1												
SUB.												
2												
SUB.												
3												
SUB.												
4												
SUB.												
5												
SUB.												
6												
SUB.												
7												
SUB.												
8												
SUB.												
9												
SUB.												
10												
SUB.												
11												
SUB.												
12												
SUB.												
13												
SUB.												
14												
SUB.												
15												
SUB.												
16												
SUB.												
17												
SUB.												TOTALS

Each inning cell shows: 1B 2B 3B HR BB with a baseball diamond.

INNING TOTALS	RUNS									
	HITS									
	ERRORS									
	LEFT ON BASE									

AB	R	H	RBI	BB	SO		PLAYER #			
							1	1	1	1
							2	2	2	2
							3	3	3	3
							4	4	4	4
							5	5	5	5
							6	6	6	6
							7	7	7	7
							8	8	8	8
							9	9	9	9
							10	10	10	10
							11	11	11	11
							12	12	12	12
							13	13	13	13
							14	14	14	14
							15	15	15	15
							16	16	16	16
							17	17	17	17
							18	18	18	18
							19	19	19	19
							20	20	20	20
							21	21	21	21
							22	22	22	22
							23	23	23	23
							24	24	24	24
							25	25	25	25
							26	26	26	26
							27	27	27	27
							28	28	28	28
							29	29	29	29
							30	30	30	30
							31	31	31	31
							32	32	32	32
							33	33	33	33
							34	34	34	34
							35	35	35	35
							36	36	36	36
							37	37	37	37
							38	38	38	38
							39	39	39	39
							40	40	40	40
							41	41	41	41
							42	42	42	42
							43	43	43	43
							44	44	44	44
							45	45	45	45
							46	46	46	46
							47	47	47	47
							48	48	48	48
							49	49	49	49
							50	50	50	50
							51	51	51	51
							52	52	52	52
							53	53	53	53
							54	54	54	54
							55	55	55	55
							56	56	56	56
							57	57	57	57
							58	58	58	58
							59	59	59	59
							60	60	60	60
							61	61	61	61
							62	62	62	62
							63	63	63	63
							64	64	64	64
							65	65	65	65
							66	66	66	66
							67	67	67	67
							68	68	68	68
							69	69	69	69
							70	70	70	70
							71	71	71	71
							72	72	72	72
							73	73	73	73
							74	74	74	74
							75	75	75	75
							76	76	76	76
							77	77	77	77
							78	78	78	78
							79	79	79	79
							80	80	80	80
							81	81	81	81
							82	82	82	82
							83	83	83	83
							84	84	84	84
							85	85	85	85
							86	86	86	86
							87	87	87	87
							88	88	88	88
							89	89	89	89
							90	90	90	90
							91	91	91	91
							92	92	92	92
							93	93	93	93
							94	94	94	94
							95	95	95	95
							96	96	96	96
							97	97	97	97
							98	98	98	98
							99	99	99	99
							100	100	100	100

NOTES

PITCH COUNT TOTALS

!"#$	%o#"&#'#()$	$*'#()$

+($.'

-.)$'	
/(%(#.&'	

#	PITCHER	W	L	S	IP	BF	H	R	ER	BB	SO
	TOTALS										

PITCHES BY INNING	1	2	3	4	5	6	7	8	9
TOTALS									

NOTES

FINAL SCORE		
HOME		VISITOR
	RUNS	
	HITS	
	ERRORS	
UMPIRES		
SCORER		

TEAM LINE UP

TEAM	OPPOSING TEAM
COACH	COACH

	NO.	STARTERS	POS.
1			
2			
3			
4			
5			
6			
7			
8			
9			
10			
11			
12			
13			
14			
15			
16			
17			

NO.	SUBSTITUTES	POS

NOTES
DATE	TIME	FIELD

TEAM LINE UP

TEAM	OPPOSING TEAM
COACH	COACH

	NO.	STARTERS	POS.
1			
2			
3			
4			
5			
6			
7			
8			
9			
10			
11			
12			
13			
14			
15			
16			
17			

NO.	SUBSTITUTES	POS

NOTES		
DATE	TIME	FIELD

BASEBALL / SOFTBALL SCORESHEET

	#	PLAYER	POS	1	2	3	4	5	6	7	8	9	
1													
SUB.													
2													
SUB.													
3													
SUB.													
4													
SUB.													
5													
SUB.													
6													
SUB.													
7													
SUB.													
8													
SUB.													
9													
SUB.													
10													
SUB.													
11													
SUB.													
12													
SUB.													
13													
SUB.													
14													
SUB.													
15													
SUB.													
16													
SUB.													
17													TOTALS
SUB.													

INNING TOTALS	RUNS									
	HITS									
	ERRORS									
	LEFT ON BASE									

AB	R	H	RBI	BB	SO	PLAYER #			

PLAYER #

1	1	1	1
2	2	2	2
3	3	3	3
4	4	4	4
5	5	5	5
6	6	6	6
7	7	7	7
8	8	8	8
9	9	9	9
10	10	10	10
11	11	11	11
12	12	12	12
13	13	13	13
14	14	14	14
15	15	15	15
16	16	16	16
17	17	17	17
18	18	18	18
19	19	19	19
20	20	20	20
21	21	21	21
22	22	22	22
23	23	23	23
24	24	24	24
25	25	25	25
26	26	26	26
27	27	27	27
28	28	28	28
29	29	29	29
30	30	30	30
31	31	31	31
32	32	32	32
33	33	33	33
34	34	34	34
35	35	35	35
36	36	36	36
37	37	37	37
38	38	38	38
39	39	39	39
40	40	40	40
41	41	41	41
42	42	42	42
43	43	43	43
44	44	44	44
45	45	45	45
46	46	46	46
47	47	47	47
48	48	48	48
49	49	49	49
50	50	50	50
51	51	51	51
52	52	52	52
53	53	53	53
54	54	54	54
55	55	55	55
56	56	56	56
57	57	57	57
58	58	58	58
59	59	59	59
60	60	60	60
61	61	61	61
62	62	62	62
63	63	63	63
64	64	64	64
65	65	65	65
66	66	66	66
67	67	67	67
68	68	68	68
69	69	69	69
70	70	70	70
71	71	71	71
72	72	72	72
73	73	73	73
74	74	74	74
75	75	75	75
76	76	76	76
77	77	77	77
78	78	78	78
79	79	79	79
80	80	80	80
81	81	81	81
82	82	82	82
83	83	83	83
84	84	84	84
85	85	85	85
86	86	86	86
87	87	87	87
88	88	88	88
89	89	89	89
90	90	90	90
91	91	91	91
92	92	92	92
93	93	93	93
94	94	94	94
95	95	95	95
96	96	96	96
97	97	97	97
98	98	98	98
99	99	99	99
100	100	100	100

NOTES

PITCH COUNT TOTALS

#	PITCHER	W	L	S	IP	BF	H	R	ER	BB	SO
	TOTALS										

PITCHES BY INNING	1	2	3	4	5	6	7	8	9
TOTALS									

NOTES

FINAL SCORE

HOME			VISITOR
	RUNS		
	HITS		
	ERRORS		

UMPIRES	
SCORER	

TEAM LINE UP

TEAM	OPPOSING TEAM
COACH	COACH

	NO.	STARTERS	POS.		NO.	SUBSTITUTES	POS
1							
2							
3							
4							
5							
6							
7							
8							
9							
10							
11							
12							
13							
14							
15							
16							
17							

NOTES

DATE	TIME	FIELD

TEAM LINE UP

TEAM	OPPOSING TEAM
COACH	COACH

	NO.	STARTERS	POS.		NO.	SUBSTITUTES	POS
1							
2							
3							
4							
5							
6							
7							
8							
9							
10							
11							
12							
13							
14							
15							
16							
17							

NOTES

DATE	TIME	FIELD

BASEBALL / SOFTBALL SCORESHEET

	#	PLAYER	POS	1	2	3	4	5	6	7	8	9
1												
SUB.												
2												
SUB.												
3												
SUB.												
4												
SUB.												
5												
SUB.												
6												
SUB.												
7												
SUB.												
8												
SUB.												
9												
SUB.												
10												
SUB.												
11												
SUB.												
12												
SUB.												
13												
SUB.												
14												
SUB.												
15												
SUB.												
16												
SUB.												
17												
SUB.												TOTALS

Each batting cell contains: 1B 2B 3B HR BB with a baseball diamond

INNING TOTALS	RUNS									
	HITS									
	ERRORS									
	LEFT ON BASE									

AB	R	H	RBI	BB	SO	PLAYER #			
						1	1	1	1
						2	2	2	2
						3	3	3	3
						4	4	4	4
						5	5	5	5
						6	6	6	6
						7	7	7	7
						8	8	8	8
						9	9	9	9
						10	10	10	10
						11	11	11	11
						12	12	12	12
						13	13	13	13
						14	14	14	14
						15	15	15	15
						16	16	16	16
						17	17	17	17
						18	18	18	18
						19	19	19	19
						20	20	20	20
						21	21	21	21
						22	22	22	22
						23	23	23	23
						24	24	24	24
						25	25	25	25
						26	26	26	26
						27	27	27	27
						28	28	28	28
						29	29	29	29
						30	30	30	30
						31	31	31	31
						32	32	32	32
						33	33	33	33
						34	34	34	34
						35	35	35	35
						36	36	36	36
						37	37	37	37
						38	38	38	38
						39	39	39	39
						40	40	40	40
						41	41	41	41
						42	42	42	42
						43	43	43	43
						44	44	44	44
						45	45	45	45
						46	46	46	46
						47	47	47	47
						48	48	48	48
						49	49	49	49
						50	50	50	50
						51	51	51	51
						52	52	52	52
						53	53	53	53
						54	54	54	54
						55	55	55	55
						56	56	56	56
						57	57	57	57
						58	58	58	58
						59	59	59	59
						60	60	60	60
						61	61	61	61
						62	62	62	62
						63	63	63	63
						64	64	64	64
						65	65	65	65
						66	66	66	66
						67	67	67	67
						68	68	68	68
						69	69	69	69
						70	70	70	70
						71	71	71	71
						72	72	72	72
						73	73	73	73
						74	74	74	74
						75	75	75	75
						76	76	76	76
						77	77	77	77
						78	78	78	78
						79	79	79	79
						80	80	80	80
						81	81	81	81
						82	82	82	82
						83	83	83	83
						84	84	84	84
						85	85	85	85
						86	86	86	86
						87	87	87	87
						88	88	88	88
						89	89	89	89
						90	90	90	90
						91	91	91	91
						92	92	92	92
						93	93	93	93
						94	94	94	94
						95	95	95	95
						96	96	96	96
						97	97	97	97
						98	98	98	98
						99	99	99	99
						100	100	100	100

NOTES

PITCH COUNT TOTALS

#	PITCHER	W	L	S	IP	BF	H	R	ER	BB	SO
	TOTALS										

PITCHES BY INNING	1	2	3	4	5	6	7	8	9
TOTALS									

NOTES

FINAL SCORE		
HOME		VISITOR
	RUNS	
	HITS	
	ERRORS	
UMPIRES		
SCORER		

TEAM LINE UP

TEAM	OPPOSING TEAM
COACH	COACH

	NO.	STARTERS	POS.		NO.	SUBSTITUTES	POS
1							
2							
3							
4							
5							
6							
7							
8							
9							
10							
11							
12							
13							
14							
15							
16							
17							

NOTES

DATE	TIME	FIELD

TEAM LINE UP

TEAM		OPPOSING TEAM	
COACH		COACH	

	NO.	STARTERS	POS.
1			
2			
3			
4			
5			
6			
7			
8			
9			
10			
11			
12			
13			
14			
15			
16			
17			

NO.	SUBSTITUTES	POS

NOTES

DATE	TIME	FIELD

BASEBALL / SOFTBALL SCORESHEET

	#	PLAYER	POS	1	2	3	4	5	6	7	8	9
1												
SUB.												
2												
SUB.												
3												
SUB.												
4												
SUB.												
5												
SUB.												
6												
SUB.												
7												
SUB.												
8												
SUB.												
9												
SUB.												
10												
SUB.												
11												
SUB.												
12												
SUB.												
13												
SUB.												
14												
SUB.												
15												
SUB.												
16												
SUB.												
17												
SUB.												TOTALS

(Each inning cell is labeled 1B 2B 3B HR BB with a baseball diamond diagram.)

INNING TOTALS	RUNS									
	HITS									
	ERRORS									
	LEFT ON BASE									

AB	R	H	RBI	BB	SO	PLAYER #			
						1 2 3 4 5 6 7 8 9 10 ...			

						PLAYER #

Player # columns (four columns) numbered 1 through 100.

NOTES

PITCH COUNT
TOTALS

#	PITCHER	W	L	S	IP	BF	H	R	ER	BB	SO
	TOTALS										

PITCHES BY INNING	1	2	3	4	5	6	7	8	9
TOTALS									

NOTES

FINAL SCORE	
HOME	VISITOR
	RUNS	
	HITS	
	ERRORS	
UMPIRES	
SCORER	

TEAM LINE UP

TEAM		OPPOSING TEAM	
COACH		COACH	

	NO.	STARTERS	POS.
1			
2			
3			
4			
5			
6			
7			
8			
9			
10			
11			
12			
13			
14			
15			
16			
17			

NO.	SUBSTITUTES	POS

NOTES		
DATE	TIME	FIELD

TEAM LINE UP

TEAM	OPPOSING TEAM
COACH	COACH

	NO.	STARTERS	POS.
1			
2			
3			
4			
5			
6			
7			
8			
9			
10			
11			
12			
13			
14			
15			
16			
17			

NO.	SUBSTITUTES	POS

NOTES		
DATE	TIME	FIELD

BASEBALL / SOFTBALL SCORESHEET

	#	PLAYER	POS	1	2	3	4	5	6	7	8	9	
1													
SUB.													
2													
SUB.													
3													
SUB.													
4													
SUB.													
5													
SUB.													
6													
SUB.													
7													
SUB.													
8													
SUB.													
9													
SUB.													
10													
SUB.													
11													
SUB.													
12													
SUB.													
13													
SUB.													
14													
SUB.													
15													
SUB.													
16													
SUB.													
17													
SUB.													TOTALS

INNING TOTALS	RUNS										
	HITS										
	ERRORS										
	LEFT ON BASE										

AB	R	H	RBI	BB	SO	PLAYER #			
						1	1	1	1
						2	2	2	2
						3	3	3	3
						4	4	4	4
						5	5	5	5
						6	6	6	6
						7	7	7	7
						8	8	8	8
						9	9	9	9
						10	10	10	10
						11	11	11	11
						12	12	12	12
						13	13	13	13
						14	14	14	14
						15	15	15	15
						16	16	16	16
						17	17	17	17
						18	18	18	18
						19	19	19	19
						20	20	20	20
						21	21	21	21
						22	22	22	22
						23	23	23	23
						24	24	24	24
						25	25	25	25
						26	26	26	26
						27	27	27	27
						28	28	28	28
						29	29	29	29
						30	30	30	30
						31	31	31	31
						32	32	32	32
						33	33	33	33
						34	34	34	34
						35	35	35	35
						36	36	36	36
						37	37	37	37
						38	38	38	38
						39	39	39	39
						40	40	40	40
						41	41	41	41
						42	42	42	42
						43	43	43	43
						44	44	44	44
						45	45	45	45
						46	46	46	46
						47	47	47	47
						48	48	48	48
						49	49	49	49
						50	50	50	50
						51	51	51	51
						52	52	52	52
						53	53	53	53
						54	54	54	54
						55	55	55	55
						56	56	56	56
						57	57	57	57
						58	58	58	58
						59	59	59	59
						60	60	60	60
						61	61	61	61
						62	62	62	62
						63	63	63	63
						64	64	64	64
						65	65	65	65
						66	66	66	66
						67	67	67	67
						68	68	68	68
						69	69	69	69
						70	70	70	70
						71	71	71	71
						72	72	72	72
						73	73	73	73
						74	74	74	74
						75	75	75	75
						76	76	76	76
						77	77	77	77
						78	78	78	78
						79	79	79	79
						80	80	80	80
						81	81	81	81
						82	82	82	82
						83	83	83	83
						84	84	84	84
						85	85	85	85
						86	86	86	86
						87	87	87	87
						88	88	88	88
						89	89	89	89
						90	90	90	90
						91	91	91	91
						92	92	92	92
						93	93	93	93
						94	94	94	94
						95	95	95	95
						96	96	96	96
						97	97	97	97
						98	98	98	98
						99	99	99	99
						100	100	100	100

NOTES

PITCH COUNT
TOTALS

#	PITCHER	W	L	S	IP	BF	H	R	ER	BB	SO
	TOTALS										

PITCHES BY INNING	1	2	3	4	5	6	7	8	9
TOTALS									

NOTES

FINAL SCORE	
HOME	VISITOR
	RUNS	
	HITS	
	ERRORS	
UMPIRES	
SCORER	

TEAM LINE UP

TEAM	OPPOSING TEAM
COACH	COACH

	NO.	STARTERS	POS.
1			
2			
3			
4			
5			
6			
7			
8			
9			
10			
11			
12			
13			
14			
15			
16			
17			

NO.	SUBSTITUTES	POS

NOTES

DATE	TIME	FIELD

TEAM LINE UP

TEAM	OPPOSING TEAM
COACH	COACH

	NO.	STARTERS	POS.		NO.	SUBSTITUTES	POS
1							
2							
3							
4							
5							
6							
7							
8							
9							
10							
11							
12							
13							
14							
15							
16							
17							

NOTES

DATE	TIME	FIELD

BASEBALL / SOFTBALL SCORESHEET

	#	PLAYER	POS	1	2	3	4	5	6	7	8	9	
1													
SUB.													
2													
SUB.													
3													
SUB.													
4													
SUB.													
5													
SUB.													
6													
SUB.													
7													
SUB.													
8													
SUB.													
9													
SUB.													
10													
SUB.													
11													
SUB.													
12													
SUB.													
13													
SUB.													
14													
SUB.													
15													
SUB.													
16													
SUB.													
17													TOTALS
SUB.													

Each inning cell is marked: 1B 2B 3B HR BB

INNING TOTALS	RUNS										
	HITS										
	ERRORS										
	LEFT ON BASE										

AB	R	H	RBI	BB	SO		PLAYER #		

<table>
<tr><th>AB</th><th>R</th><th>H</th><th>RBI</th><th>BB</th><th>SO</th></tr>
</table>

PLAYER #

(Player number columns, numbered 1–100 repeated in four columns)

NOTES

PITCH COUNT
TOTALS

!"#$ %&#"&#"#()$ $*!"#()$

+($,!

-.)$'

A'%(#.&'

#	PITCHER	W	L	S	IP	BF	H	R	ER	BB	SO
	TOTALS										

PITCHES BY INNING		1	2	3	4	5	6	7	8	9
TOTALS										

NOTES

FINAL SCORE	
HOME	VISITOR
	RUNS	
	HITS	
	ERRORS	
UMPIRES	
SCORER	

TEAM LINE UP

TEAM	OPPOSING TEAM
COACH	COACH

	NO.	STARTERS	POS.
1			
2			
3			
4			
5			
6			
7			
8			
9			
10			
11			
12			
13			
14			
15			
16			
17			

NO.	SUBSTITUTES	POS

NOTES

DATE	TIME	FIELD

TEAM LINE UP

TEAM	OPPOSING TEAM
COACH	COACH

	NO.	STARTERS	POS.		NO.	SUBSTITUTES	POS
1							
2							
3							
4							
5							
6							
7							
8							
9							
10							
11							
12							
13							
14							
15							
16							
17							

NOTES		
DATE	TIME	FIELD

BASEBALL / SOFTBALL SCORESHEET

	#	PLAYER	POS	1	2	3	4	5	6	7	8	9
1												
SUB.												
2												
SUB.												
3												
SUB.												
4												
SUB.												
5												
SUB.												
6												
SUB.												
7												
SUB.												
8												
SUB.												
9												
SUB.												
10												
SUB.												
11												
SUB.												
12												
SUB.												
13												
SUB.												
14												
SUB.												
15												
SUB.												
16												
SUB.												
17												TOTALS
SUB.												

Each diamond cell labeled: 1B 2B 3B HR BB

INNING TOTALS	RUNS									
	HITS									
	ERRORS									
	LEFT ON BASE									

AB	R	H	RBI	BB	SO	PLAYER #			
						1	1	1	1
						2	2	2	2
						3	3	3	3
						4	4	4	4
						5	5	5	5
						6	6	6	6
						7	7	7	7
						8	8	8	8
						9	9	9	9
						10	10	10	10
						11	11	11	11
						12	12	12	12
						13	13	13	13
						14	14	14	14
						15	15	15	15
						16	16	16	16
						17	17	17	17
						18	18	18	18
						19	19	19	19
						20	20	20	20
						21	21	21	21
						22	22	22	22
						23	23	23	23
						24	24	24	24
						25	25	25	25
						26	26	26	26
						27	27	27	27
						28	28	28	28
						29	29	29	29
						30	30	30	30
						31	31	31	31
						32	32	32	32
						33	33	33	33
						34	34	34	34
						35	35	35	35
						36	36	36	36
						37	37	37	37
						38	38	38	38
						39	39	39	39
						40	40	40	40
						41	41	41	41
						42	42	42	42
						43	43	43	43
						44	44	44	44
						45	45	45	45
						46	46	46	46
						47	47	47	47
						48	48	48	48
						49	49	49	49
						50	50	50	50
						51	51	51	51
						52	52	52	52
						53	53	53	53
						54	54	54	54
						55	55	55	55
						56	56	56	56
						57	57	57	57
						58	58	58	58
						59	59	59	59
						60	60	60	60
						61	61	61	61
						62	62	62	62
						63	63	63	63
						64	64	64	64
						65	65	65	65
						66	66	66	66
						67	67	67	67
						68	68	68	68
						69	69	69	69
						70	70	70	70
						71	71	71	71
						72	72	72	72
						73	73	73	73
						74	74	74	74
						75	75	75	75
						76	76	76	76
						77	77	77	77
						78	78	78	78
						79	79	79	79
						80	80	80	80
						81	81	81	81
						82	82	82	82
						83	83	83	83
						84	84	84	84
						85	85	85	85
						86	86	86	86
						87	87	87	87
						88	88	88	88
						89	89	89	89
						90	90	90	90
						91	91	91	91
						92	92	92	92
						93	93	93	93
						94	94	94	94
						95	95	95	95
						96	96	96	96
						97	97	97	97
						98	98	98	98
						99	99	99	99
						100	100	100	100

NOTES

PITCH COUNT
TOTALS

!"#$	%u#"&#'#()$	$*'!"#()$
‐($.!		
‐.)$'		
/(%(#.&'		

#	PITCHER	W	L	S	IP	BF	H	R	ER	BB	SO
	TOTALS										

PITCHES BY INNING	1	2	3	4	5	6	7	8	9
TOTALS									

NOTES

FINAL SCORE			
HOME			VISITOR
	RUNS		
	HITS		
	ERRORS		
UMPIRES			
SCORER			